# Electronics for Schools

# Electronics for Schools

R. A. Sparkes B.Sc., C.Eng., M.I.E.R.E. M.Inst.P.
Notre Dame College of Education,
Bearsden, Glasgow

Hutchinson Educational Ltd
3 Fitzroy Square London W1

London Melbourne Sydney
Auckland Wellington Johannesburg Cape Town
and agencies throughout the world

First published 1972

ISBN 0 09 112781 5

Typeset by D P Press Ltd, Sevenoaks
Printed in Great Britain by Anchor Press, and
bound by Wm. Brendon, both of Tiptree, Essex.

# Contents

# Preface

The author has been concerned with the in-service training of schoolteachers for several years, mostly in electronics. During this time it became apparent that there was no suitable book for introducing electronics to school-children in a simple and practical way. With the encouragement of those teachers who came to courses in Applied Science/Engineering Project Work for Schools, an elementary introduction to electronics for 11 to 14 year-old schoolchildren was developed, and it is from that scheme that this book has been produced.

This book is *not* a series of 'recipes' for making electronic gadgets. Apart from their doubtful educational value, such 'recipes' are not for beginners. For one thing, if one of these gadgets is made, which then fails to work, what can be done to put it right? Secondly, what if the circuit described is not quite what is wanted? A flashing light circuit may be described which gives one flash every second: how can it be adapted to give two flashes per second?

Both of these problems are overcome if the constructor understands how the circuit should work. Then he can discover what to do if the current fails to work, and also change the components to make the circuit work differently. The emphasis in this book is thus, on getting to know what components will do, and how they behave in the most common circuits in electronics. Then, and only then, should the constructor start following recipes. There are a few such ideas given in the latter part of this book, but the main part is the 'course' in basic electronics, given in the first eight chapters. For this it is essential that the constructor has the basic kit of parts and builds up each circuit in turn.

The basic kit of components for the first eight chapters is as follows:

| Number needed | Component |
| --- | --- |
| 1 | 10 Ω Resistor (½W) |
| 1 | 47Ω Resistor (½W) |
| 1 | 100Ω Resistor (½W) |
| 3 | 1kΩ Resistor (½W) |
| 1 | 4·7 kΩ Resistor (½W) |
| 2 | 10 kΩ Resistor (½W) |
| 3 | 100 kΩ Resistor (½W) |
| 1 | Thermistor (Type TH3) |
| 1 | 10kΩ Variable Resistor |
| 1 | 220 pF Capacitor |
| 2 | 0·01 μF Capacitor |
| 2 | 0·1 μF Capacitor |
| 3 | 2 μF Capacitor |

| | |
|---|---|
| 2 | 100 $\mu$F Capacitor |
| 1 | 500 pF Variable Capacitor |
| 1 | 1GP7 Diode |
| 1 | M.E.S. Bulb (6V 0·06A) |
| 1 | M.E.S. Bulb-holder |
| 1 | Knob |
| 1 | Ferrite Rod (6" x $\frac{3}{8}$ ") |
| 1 | Battery clip for PP6 battery |
| 1 | Battery (PP6) |
| 4 | Crocodile clips |
| 3 | Transistors (ZTX 300 or BC 108) |
| 2 (or 1) | Crystal Earpieces |
| 1 | Light dependent resistor (ORP 12) |
| | Wire, solder, softboard, pins and so on. |

A list of places where these components may be obtained is provided in *Notes for the Teacher* (Appendix, page 60). A kit containing the above components, excluding the softboard and brass pins, may be obtained from NESLO Electronics; alternatively the components may be obtained from R.S. Components Ltd. (Details, see page 60).

We have continuously tried to keep the cost of the course to a minimum. We have avoided the use of oscillators, oscilloscopes and expensive multi-meters. This means that we have not been able to explain such phenomena as alternating current, a resonant circuits, biasing the transistor, and so on, in a traditional way, but we have relied instead on analogies with mechanical phenomena, especially with the behaviour of water. Where a teacher does have the time and the relevant apparatus, he could usefully employ them in explaining the behaviour of circuits more fully.

The method of construction used is by soldering onto brass pins pushed into softboard, as we have found this to be the cheapest and least time consuming method available. The basic course is adaptable to 'no-soldering' methods of construction and a few of these are mentioned in *Notes for the Teacher* (Appendix, page 60). However, if pupils are to graduate to building circuits in a more compact way (for example, on printed circuit boards), they must have considerable practice in soldering beforehand. It might even be argued that pupils should learn the art of making good soldered joints anyway, just as they are taught the correct use of a tenon-saw or hand-drill in other craft subjects.

We have also tried to use the minimum number of components. The circuits have been devised to use the same components over and over again. For instance, only one sort of transistor is used throughout. To this end, we have sometimes not followed standard practice initially, but the transistion to more conventional circuits is made in the projects.

The author wishes to thank his colleagues of the former Rugby College of Engineering Technology for their help and encouragement in the development of this book, especially those teachers who have attended the courses in electronics in the Education Unit of the College.

*R. A. Sparkes*
*Notre Dame College of Education*
*Bearsden, Glasgow*

*August 1972*

# 1 Direct Currents

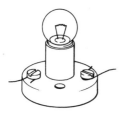

Look at this picture of a bulb and its holder!
We are going to learn how to make the bulb light up.
First take two pieces of bare tinned copper wire, each about 3 cm long.

Fig. 1

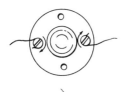

Undo each screw of the bulb holder about two turns.
Bend the end of each wire round its screw in a *clockwise* direction and then tighten the screws (Why a *clockwise* direction?)

Fig. 2

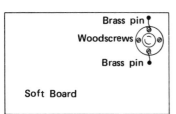

Fix the bulb holder to the sheet of soft-board with two small wood-screws. Notice that it is placed in the top right-hand corner of the board.

Push two brass pins into the soft board with the help of pliers, and solder the connecting wires onto these pins as in the diagram. If you do not know how to solder, you must read the chapter on *Soldering Techniques* at the end of this book (See Appendix III on page 58).

Fig. 3

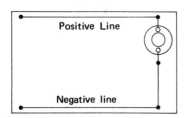

Now push three more pins into the soft-board as shown, and solder bare tinned copper wire to join up the pins as in the diagram.

The wire at the top of the board is called the *positive line*, because we are going to connect it to the positive pole (+) of the battery.

The wire at the bottom of the board is called the *negative line*, because we are going to connect it to the negative pole (−) of the battery.

Fig. 4

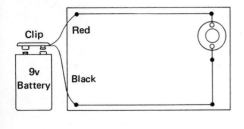

**Fig. 5**

Remove about 0·5 cm of the plastic from the end of each lead of the battery clip using wire strippers.

Solder the *red* lead to the *positive line*.

Solder the *black* lead to the *negative line*.

Now clip the battery onto the battery clip: the bulb should light up. If it does, then all is well. Unclip the battery and continue.

If the bulb does not light up, turn to the chapter on *What Went Wrong?* at the back of the book (See Appendix IV, page 59). You should turn to this chapter *whenever* you cannot get a circuit to work in the way that it should. *Never* proceed to the next circuit until you have got the present one working properly.

To prevent the battery from wearing out (going 'flat'), *always disconnect the battery when you are not actually using it, and especially before going on to the next circuit!*

**Fig. 6**

Electricity is a little bit like water flowing along a hosepipe. The water is 'pushed' along the pipe by the pressure of water in the tap. Electricity is 'pushed' along a wire by the *voltage* from a battery.

Some batteries give a bigger 'push' than others, that is, they have a bigger voltage, which is measured in *volts*. We are using a 9 volt battery, whereas most cycle lamps use a 3 volt battery. With water the greater the pressure in the tap, then the greater the amount of water which flows along the pipe. With electricity, the greater the voltage of the battery, then the greater the flow of electricity along the wire. We call this flow of electricity the *electric current*, or just simply the *current*.

The sort of current coming from a battery always flows in one direction only, it is called *direct current*. Water can flow along the hosepipe and spill out onto the ground when it reaches the end. Electric current is not like this; it can only flow in a *complete circuit*. We say that it flows out of the positive pole of the battery, along the positive line to the bulb, through the bulb, down to the negative line and back to the negative pole of the battery. That is why we are so concerned not to get any poor connections in our circuit. If there are any breaks at all, then the current will not flow.

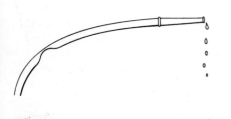

**Fig. 7**

Now think of what happens to the water in the hosepipe if somebody stands on the pipe. The flow of water is reduced to a mere trickle. The pressure of the water in the tap has not changed, but the flow of water has been reduced nevertheless.

The same thing can happen with electric current. Some things, which we call *components*, such as the bulb, act like the constriction in the hosepipe; they reduce the amount of current flowing in the wires. We say that they have *resistance* to the flow of current. The battery is still 'pushing' as hard as before, but the resistance of the component is reducing the current.

Fig. 8

Now take a close look at the bulb. Inside the glass case there is a very thin wire, called a *filament*. It is when the current squeezes through this filament, that it feels the resistance and so produces heat. The filament becomes white hot and so produces light.

We are going to add more resistance to our circuit to see what happens, but we should be able to guess already. The more current that we can get to flow through the filament of the bulb, then the brighter it will become. We are in fact already doing this, because the bulb we are using was made to work from a 6 volt battery. (It also means that the bulb will not last very long, it will wear out quicker, which is another reason why you were told to take the battery out of the circuit when you are not actually using it.)

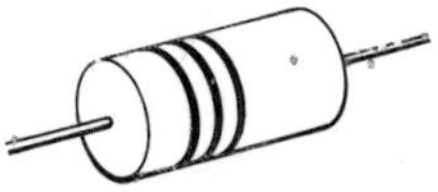

---

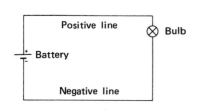

Fig. 9

The less current that flows through the bulb then the dimmer it will become. Now we have just been told that adding resistance to a circuit should reduce the current. This is what we are going to do later, but first how do we know *how much* resistance we have got?

The resistance is measured in *ohms*. The components which have this resistance are called *resistors*. We can get resistors from a few ohms to millions of ohms. So that we do not have to write down too many noughts we use a shorthand notation.

$$1\ 000 \text{ ohms} = 1 \text{ kilohm}$$
$$1\ 000\ 000 \text{ ohms} = 1 \text{ megohm}$$

This can get a bit difficult when we have a resistor like 4 700 ohms, we like to call it 4·7 kilohms. Can you see that this means the same thing?

Also instead of writing the word 'ohms', we use the symbol $\Omega$. Similarly 'k$\Omega$' stands for kilohms and 'M$\Omega$' for megohms.

Every resistor is 'colour coded' so that we know what its resistance is. The meaning of these coloured bands is explained in Appendix I on page 56.

We said that the bulb has resistance also. Its resistance is about 100$\Omega$, which is quite small for electronic circuits. Usually the resistors we use are about 1 k$\Omega$ or more.

---

Fig. 10

This picture is called a *circuit diagram*. It tells us exactly the same as Fig. 5, but it is more compact.

Instead of drawing pictures of the battery, bulb etc. we use a special *circuit symbol* for each component. Notice the symbols used for the battery and the bulb. All the circuit symbols used in this book are listed in Appendix II (page 56.)

Notice that all the unnecessary details have been omitted from the circuit diagram. (No pins, bulb holder, soft-board or battery clips are included.) Only the essential parts are shown. Later on, when you have learned to read circuit diagrams, we shall use them entirely, instead of drawing pictures like Fig. 5.

3

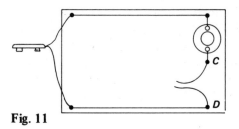

**Fig. 11**

Remove the wire connecting pins *C* and *D*. This is best done by cutting the wire with wire-cutters as close to the pins as possible, rather than trying to unsolder them.

Take two pieces of *flexible* plastic-covered wire each about 15 cm long. Strip off 0·5 cm of plastic from *both* ends of each wire. Solder the wires onto pins *C* and *D* as in the diagram.

**Fig. 12**

Connect crocodile clips onto the other ends of these wires. Thread the wire through the hole, wrap the bared end round the screw as before, and tighten the screw.

We will put various *resistors* between these clips to see what happens, but first we must see if we still have a complete circuit. Touch the clips together for a short time and see if the bulb still lights up.

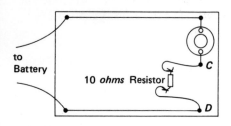

**Fig. 13**

Clip the 10 ohms resistor firmly between the crocodile clips as shown. This resistor has the coloured bands brown, black, black.

Notice that the bulb still glows, but not as brightly as before. The resistance we have introduced has reduced the current.

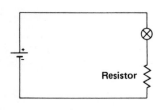

**Fig. 14**

This is the circuit diagram of Fig. 13. Notice the symbol for the resistor.

Remove the 10 ohms resistor and replace it with the 47 ohms resistor (yellow, purple, black). The bulb will be even less bright than before.

Remove the 47Ω resistor and replace it with the 100Ω resistor (brown, black, brown). The current is now so small that the bulb hardly glows at all.

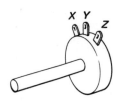

**Fig. 15**

Remove the 100Ω resistor: we shall replace it with a variable resistor. This has three terminals labelled *X*, *Y* and *Z*.

The resistance between terminals *X* and *Z* is always the same, (in this case it is 10 kΩ), but the resistance between terminals *Y* and *Z* can be varied from zero ohms (when the shaft is turned fully anti-clockwise), to 10 kΩ (when the shaft is turned fully clockwise).

The volume control of a radio set is a variable resistor just like ours.

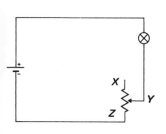

**Fig. 16**

Attach the crocodile clips of leads $C$ and $D$ to the terminals $Y$ and $Z$ of the variable resistor, (terminal $X$ is not used). Fix a knob to the shaft of the variable resistor and turn this knob to vary the brightness of the bulb.

Notice that turning the knob clockwise (increased resistance) leads to a dimming of the bulb (reduced current).

Notice the circuit symbol for the variable resistor in the circuit diagram.

(You may notice that the control over the brightness of the bulb is not very good. It would be much better to use a 100Ω variable resistor, if you can get hold of one. Since it is only likely to be used in this one circuit, there is no point in buying one specially.)

*Summary*

This is what we have learned so far:

Electric current can only flow in a complete circuit.

The voltage from a battery 'pushes' the current round the circuit.

The current flows out of the positive pole of the battery, round the circuit and back into the battery through the negative pole.

Resistance reduces the flow of current in a circuit.

# 2 Semiconductor Devices

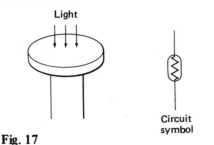

Fig. 17

**(a) The light dependent resistor**

As its name suggests this is a device which changes its resistance according to the amount of light falling on it. In bright sunlight it has a resistance of about 100 ohms or less. In total darkness its resistance is more than 100 k$\Omega$.

We shall call this device an *L.D.R.* for short.

Since it is quite the most expensive component we shall use, be very careful with it. Do not bend the legs of the *L.D.R.* or they might break off.

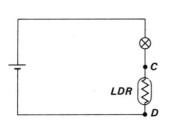

Fig. 18

Clip the *L.D.R.* between the crocodile clips of leads *C* and *D*. In the dark the resistance of the *L.D.R.* is *high* so the current will be *low*, and the bulb will be *off*. In bright sunlight or by a bright lamp the *L.D.R.* resistance is *low*, the current will be *high* and the bulb will be *on*.

You may like to think of the *L.D.R.* as a variable resistor which alters its resistance when the level of light alters. We shall write down a simple rule to remind you how it does this. There will be several such rules in this book, and we shall refer back to them from time to time.

Rule 1 is:  brightness = low resistance

darkness  = high resistance

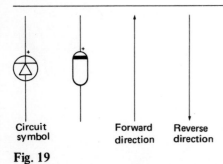

Fig. 19

**(b) The diode**

This is a device which changes its resistance depending upon the *way* the electric current flows through it.

In one direction (called the *forward* direction) the diode resistance is *low*. In the other direction (called the *reverse* direction) the resistance is *high*.

This is different from a resistor, where the resistance is the same in either direction.

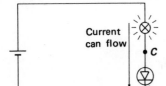

Fig. 20

Clip the diode into the circuit between the leads *C* and *D*. One end of the diode will have a black or red ring round it. This end corresponds to the + end of the circuit symbol shown in Fig. 19. Make sure that this end is clipped to lead *D*. The diode should then pass current in the forward direction, and the bulb should be bright.

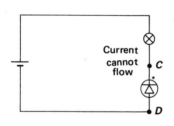

Fig. 21

Now turn the diode round so that its + end goes to lead *C*. This is the reverse direction, so the diode has a very high resistance and the bulb is *off*.

The circuit symbol has an arrow head in it. This indicates the forward direction of the diode. In Fig. 20 the current was flowing through the diode in the *same* direction as the arrowhead; now it is trying to flow in the opposite direction to the arrowhead.

It is not difficult to find out which is the forward direction of the actual diode itself. The black or red ring gives the clue. In the forward direction current flows *out of* this end.

### (c) The thermistor

This is a device which changes its resistance according to its tempeature. If the thermistor is cold, it has a high resistance. If it is hot, it has a low resistance.

Fig. 22

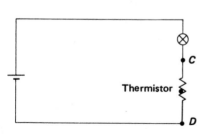

Fig. 23

Clip the thermistor onto leads *C* and *D*. In the cold the thermistor resistance is *high* so the bulb is *off*. If the thermistor is heated gently with a lighted match (or with the soldering iron) its resistance gets less, so the bulb gets brighter and brighter. Note the symbol for the thermistor.

### (d) The transistor

This is another device that can be damaged by rough handling. Again it is easy to break off the legs of the transistor by bending them.

The transistor has three legs called

the *Collector*    (*C*)
the *Base*          (*B*)
the *Emitter*       (*E*)

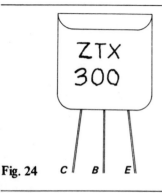

Fig. 24

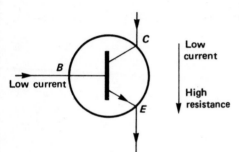

In the transistor we use, current must flow *into* the collector and *out of* the emitter. The direction of the current flow is shown by the arrowhead on the circuit symbol for the transistor. We must always connect the collector towards the positive line and the emitter towards the negative line.

There is also a small control current which flows into the base of the transistor and joins up with the main current to flow out at the emitter.

**Fig. 25**

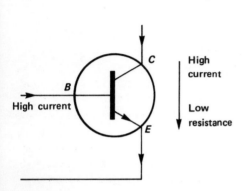

If the base current is low, then the collector current is also low, and the resistance of the transistor, between the collector and emitter leads is very high (see Fig. 25).

If the base current is larger, the collector current is high and the collector-emitter resistance is low. Generally the collector current is about 100 times bigger than the base current. This is why the transistor can be used to make circuits more sensitive, since tiny changes in the base current become big changes in collector current.

Since the transistor can be damaged if too large a base current flows into it, we always connect a resistor to the base lead, which keeps the base current within limits.

**Fig. 26**

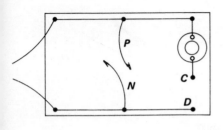

Remove the battery if you have not already done so.

Remove the flying leads $C$ and $D$ by cutting the wires as close to the pins as possible.

Resolder one of these leads about half-way along the positive line, and the other about half-way along the negative line as in the diagram. These are then called leads $P$ and $N$.

Read carefully the notes on *Soldering Techniques*, especially section 3, in Appendix III on page 58. The transistor can be damaged if it gets too hot while being soldered.

**Fig. 27**

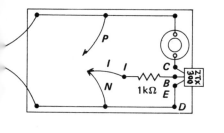

**Fig. 28**

Push two pins (B and E) into the soft-board as shown. Since we are going to solder the transistor onto these pins, do not place them too far apart.

Solder a short connection between pins E and D.

Push a pin I into the soft-board about 7 cm from pin B, and solder a 1 kΩ resistor between them ( brown, black, red).

Then solder the transistor onto the pins as follows:

The *Collector* goes to pin C

The *Base* goes to pin B

The *Emitter* goes to pin E

Make sure that you have got it the right way round, or you could damage it when you reconnect the battery.

Make up another flying lead from flexible plastic-covered wire, about 15 cm long and having a crocodile clip at one end. Solder this to pin I. We shall call this lead I. Clip the leads I and N together as in the diagram, and make sure that lead P is not touching anything.

Now clip the battery into place.

---

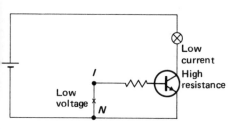

**Fig. 29**

This is the circuit diagram of Fig. 28.

The input *(I)* is connected to the negative line. Since current flows from the positive line, no current can flow into I and thence into the base of the transistor. The base current of the transistor is low, so the collector-emitter resistance is high and the collector current is low. So the bulb is *off*.

We could say that there is no voltage at I to make the current flow into the base. All these are true at the same time. Low voltage at I = low base current = low collector current = high collector-emitter resistance = bulb *off*

---

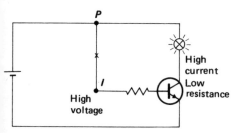

**Fig. 30**

Disconnect leads I and N and put N where it cannot touch anything. Now connect leads I and P. Figure 30 is the circuit diagram of this situation.

Since I is connected to the positive line, current can flow down the wire to I and thence into the base of the transistor. Because we have a base current there is a large collector current and the bulb is *on*.

We could say that there is a high voltage at I. In other words: high voltage at I = high base current = high collector current = low collector-emitter resistance = bulb *on*

Because this is so important we repeat the above rules again.
High voltage at $I$ = high base current = low resistance = bulb *on*
Low voltage at $I$ = low base current = high resistance = bulb *off*
This is a very important rule, we call it Rule 2.

Go back to Figs. 29 and 30 again and study what is happening.
Almost everthing that we do will use Rule 2 over and over again. You
must understand it before carrying on.

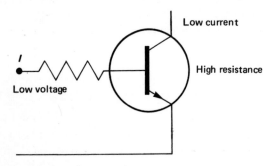

**Fig. 31**

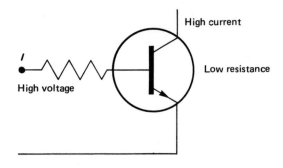

**Fig. 32**

*Summary*
This is what we have learned in Chapter 2

| Device | How it is controlled | When it has high resistance | When it has low resistance |
|---|---|---|---|
| Light dependent Resistor | By the amount of light | Dark | Light |
| Diode | By direction of current | Reverse direction | Forward direction |
| Thermistor | By temperature | Cold | Hot |
| Transistor | By the voltage at the input (I) | Low voltage Low base current | High voltage High base current |

# 3 Controlling the Transistor

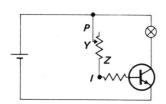

One simple way of controlling the base current of the transistor is to put a variable resistor between the clips of leads *P* and *I* as in the circuit diagram. Clip onto terminals *Y* and *Z* of the 10 kΩ variable resistor.

By *increasing* the resistance of the variable resistor, you are *reducing* the base current, so the bulb will be *less* bright.

(It would be better to use a 100 kΩ variable resistor if you can get one, since the 10 kΩ resistor is far too small to do this job properly.)

**Fig. 33**

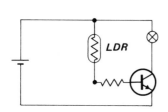

Another way to control the base current is to use the *L.D.R.* Remove the variable resistor and replace it with the *L.D.R.*

Do you remember how this works? (See Rule 1 on page 6)

Can you work out for yourself if the bulb should be *off* or *on* in the dark? Use Rule 2 on page 10.

In the dark the *L.D.R.* has a high resistance, so it only passes a low current. The base current is low, therefore, and the bulb is *off*.

**Fig. 34**

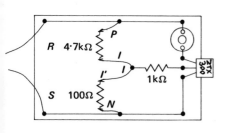

The methods of controlling the transistor of Fig. 33 and Fig. 34 are not very good. A much better way is to control the *voltage* at the input (*I*).

Make up another flying lead with crocodile clip, and solder this onto pin *I*. We now have two flying leads attached to pin *I*, so we shall call them *I* and *I* '.

Clip a 4·7 kΩ resistor (yellow, purple, red) between the crocodile clips of leads *I* and *P*, and 100Ω resistor (brown, black, brown) between *I* ' and *N*, as in the diagram.

The bulb is *off*.

**Fig. 35**

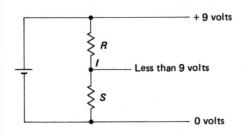

**Fig. 36**

In order to see how this works, we shall separate the two resistors (which we shall call $R$ and $S$) from the transistor. After all, we know how the transistor part works. It obeys Rule 2, which can be simplified to:

> input voltage high = bulb *on*
> input voltage low = bulb *off*

The voltage provided by the battery at $P$ is 9 volts. Some of this voltage is 'used up', as the current struggles to get through the first resistor ($R$). This means that the voltage at $I$ is less than 9 volts.

The rest of the voltage is used up as the current struggles to get through the second resistor ($S$), so that the voltage at the negative line is 0 (zero) volts.

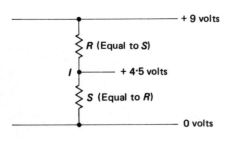

**Fig. 37**

Suppose that $R$ and $S$ were equal resistances. Then the voltage used up (or as we prefer to say, the voltage drop) across $R$ would be equal to the voltage drop across $S$. In other words the voltage at $I$ would be exactly 4·5 volts.

Notice that we have no need to draw the battery in the circuit diagram any more. We know that the line marked +9 volts must go to the positive pole of a 9 volt battery, and that the line marked 0 volts must go to the negative pole of this battery.

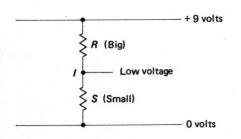

**Fig. 38**

Now suppose that $R$ is bigger than $S$.

The voltage dropped across $R$ would be bigger than the voltage dropped across $S$. This would mean that the voltage at $I$ is low.

It does not matter if we now reconnect $I$ to the transistor to get back to Fig. 35. The voltage at $I$ will still be low, and since $I$ is now the input to the transistor, it means we have a low input voltage, so the bulb is *off*.

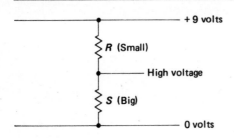

**Fig. 39**

Let us now see what would happen if $R$ is made smaller than $S$. We would now expect the voltage at $I$ to be high (since only a little voltage is dropped across $R$).

If $I$ is now reconnected to the transistor input, we would have a high input voltage and the bulb would be *on*.

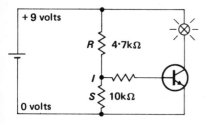

Fig. 40

Let us see if that is right.

Take out the 100Ω resistor and replace it with a 10 kΩ resistor (so that we now have $R$ smaller than $S$).

Is the bulb *on* as it should be?

There is no reason why these resistors should be fixed values, so let us now try with the variable resistor.

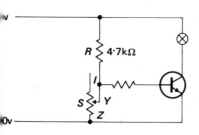

Fig. 41

Take out the 10 kΩ resistor and replace it with the 10 kΩ variable resistor (terminals $Y$ and $Z$).

When this is turned to a low resistance, $I$ becomes a low voltage and the bulb goes *off*.

When the variable resistor is turned to a high resistance, the voltage at $I$ becomes high and the bulb comes *on*.

We now have a rule for this, which we call Rule 3.

If $R$ is bigger than $S$, $I$ is at a low voltage.

If $R$ is smaller than $S$, $I$ is at a high voltage

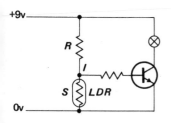

Fig. 42

We are now going to apply the ideas we have learned to make some useful circuits. In each case, see if you can work out what *should* happen, before trying it out in practice. If you *can* do this, then you are really understanding what is happening.

In the circuit of Fig. 42, the *L.D.R.* takes the place of resistor $S$, while $R$ is still the 4·7 kΩ resistor.

In the dark, what resistance does the *L.D.R.* have? (Look back to Fig. 18)

Is this bigger or smaller than $R$?

So is the voltage at $I$ *high* or *low*? (Look back to Rule 3)

So is the bulb going to come *on* or go *off* in the dark? (See Rule 2)

Now remove the variable resistor from the clips of leads $N$ and $I'$, and replace it with the *L.D.R.*

Did you work it out right? Is the bulb *on* or *off* in the dark? The correct answer is that the bulb should be *on* in the dark and *off* when it is light.

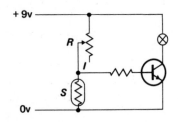

We could use the circuit of Fig. 42 to make an *automatic car parking light*, that is a light that comes on by itself when the daylight is dwindling. It would however have two disadvantages.

Firstly, we cannot control the light level at which the bulb comes on, because this happens when the resistance of the *L.D.R.* reaches about 1 kΩ.

Replace the 4·7 kΩ resistor with the 10 kΩ variable resistor. We can now alter the resistance of $R$, so that we have two controls over the voltage at $I$. The light level controls the resistance of the *L.D.R.* ($S$), and we control the variable resistor ($R$).

We can arrange it so that the bulb comes on at almost any light level. See if you can adjust the variable resistor, so that the bulb is *off*, but comes *on* when you pass your hand over the *L.D.R.*

The second disadvantage of this circuit is that it is still a bit insensitive. Later we shall see how to make this circuit so that it will detect a movement of the hand at least 1 metre away.

**Fig. 43**

How can we make this circuit work the other way, so that the bulb is *off*, but comes *on* when a hand is passed over the *L.D.R.*?

One obvious way is as follows:

Swap over the *L.D.R.* and the variable resistor, as in the diagram. In the dark the *L.D.R.* is a high resistance, so $R$ will be bigger than $S$, so $I$ will be a low voltage and the bulb will be *off.* Can you now work out what should happen in the light?

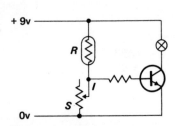

**Fig. 44**

Replace the *L.D.R.* with the thermistor. Remember that:

    hot thermistor = low resistance
    cold thermistor = high resistance

You should be able to adjust the variable resistor so that the bulb is normally *off*, but comes *on* when the thermistor is heated with a lighted match.

Later on we shall use this idea to make a *fire alarm,* but at the moment it is a little insensitive to temperature changes.

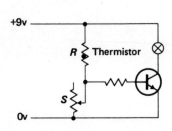

**Fig. 45**

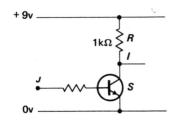

+ 9v

1kΩ    R

I

J

S

0v

**Fig. 46**

In the next chapter we shall use a 1 kΩ resistor as $R$, and another transistor as $S$.

We know that we can make the transistor be a low resistance by putting a high voltage at its input ($J$).

We can make the transistor be a high resistance by putting a low voltage at its input ($J$).

If this is not immediately obvious to you, go back to the beginning of Chapter 3 again. Unless you can understand the more simple circuits that we have done up to now, you will not be able to understand the circuits of Chapter 4.

# 4 The Invertor

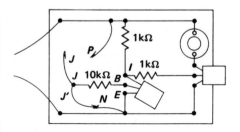

**Fig. 47**

Push in a pin $J$ about 7 cm from $I$ into the soft-board. Remove the two flying leads $I$ and $I'$ from pin $I$ and solder them onto pin $J$ (We shall now call these leads $J$ and $J'$).

Push in two more pins $B$ and $E$ as shown and solder a connection between pin $E$ and the negative line. Solder a 10 k$\Omega$ resistor between pins $J$ and $B$, and a 1 k$\Omega$ resistor between pin $I$ and the positive line.

Finally solder a transistor into place with:

the Collector to pin $I$

the Base to pin $B$

and    the Emitter to pin $E$

Clip the leads $J'$ and $N$ together.

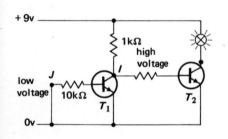

**Fig. 48**

This is the circuit diagram of Fig. 47.

Since $J$ is at a low voltage, the transistor $T_1$ is a high resistance (See Rule 2 on page 10.

This means that $I$ is a high voltage (See Rule 3 on page 13). If $I$ is a high voltage then the bulb will be *on*, (Rule 2 again). The important part of this is what happens at transistor $T_1$. Remember that if $J$ is a low voltage, $I$ is a high voltage.

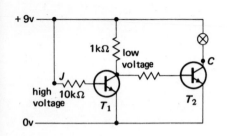

**Fig. 49**

Now release the clips of $N$ and $J'$, and connect the clips $P$ and $J$. $J$ is now at a high voltage, so the transistor $T_1$ is a low resistance and $I$ is therefore a low voltage, so the bulb is *off*.

$J$ is the *input* of transistor $T_1$, and we could call $I$ the *output* of transistor $T_1$.

We can now summarize what we have learned:

high input voltage = low output voltage

low input voltage = high output voltage

Do you see now why we call trasistor $T_1$ an *invertor?*

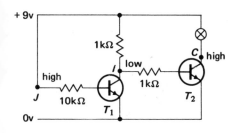

Just because transistor $T_2$ has a bulb instead of a 1 kΩ resistor connected to it does not mean that it is not an invertor.

From the point of view of transistor $T_2$, its *input* is $I$, and its *output* is $C$. It is still true that:

   high input voltage = low output voltage

   low input voltage = high output voltage

We shall make use of this idea later.

**Fig. 50**

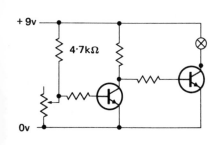

All circuits that we tried out in Figs. 41 to 45 can now be repeated by connecting the L.D.R., thermistor, etc. to the leads J and J' instead of leads I and I'. There will be two differences.

Firstly the circuits will be *more sensitive* to changes in resistance, and hence to changes in temperature and light.

Secondly they will work the opposite way. Where the bulb was previously *on* it will be *off* and vice versa. This is because transistor $T_1$ is behaving as an invertor.

We shall not give details of the circuits here, except to show what happens to the circuit of Fig. 41. You should be able to work out the others for yourself. Details of the circuits are given in Chapter 10, *Electronic Projects*, (see page 42).

**Fig. 51**

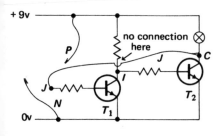

There are two special uses of the simple circuit of Fig. 49. First clip the lead $J$ onto pin $C$, that is, connect the *output* of transistor $T_2$ to the *input* of $T_1$.

The *output of T$_1$* is already connected to the *input of T$_2$* at $I$.

Lead $P$ is not used in this circuit. Lead $J'$ will not be required again, so remove it with the wire cutters.

When the clip of lead $N$ is tapped momentarily onto pin $C$, the bulb comes *on*, and stays *on*, even when the clip of lead $N$ is removed from $C$.

When $N$ is tapped momentarily onto pin $I$, the bulb goes *off* and stays *off*.

Clearly we have a circuit that behaves like a switch, that can be on or off. It is called a *bistable switch*, because it is stable in either of *two* states.

**Fig. 52**

17

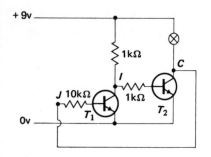

Fig. 53

When $N$ is touched onto pin $C$, $C$ becomes a low voltage.
But $J$ is connected to $C$, so it becomes a low voltage.
So $I$ becomes a high voltage (because of the invertor action of $T_1$).
So $C$ becomes a low voltage (because of the invertor action of $T_2$).
So even if $N$ is removed from $C$, $C$ is still held at a low voltage.

When $N$ is touched onto pin $I$, then $I$ becomes a low voltage, while $C$ and $J$ become a high voltage. This is exactly the opposite state.

We call one of these the *on* state and the other the *off* state.

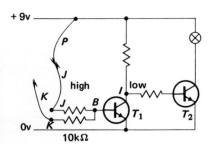

Fig. 54

The second important use of the circuit of Fig. 49 is this. First unclip lead $J$ from pin $C$. Push another pin $K$ into the board about 1 cm below pin $J$. Solder another 10 k$\Omega$ resistor between pin $K$ and pin $B$. (Be careful, since the transistor could be damaged when you solder to pin $B$). Solder a flying lead to pin $K$ (we shall call this lead $K$).

If lead $J$ is clipped onto the clip of lead $P$, the bulb goes *off*. This should not be surprising by now. After all, if $J$ is a high voltage, then $I$ will be a low voltage, and the bulb will go *off*.

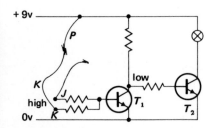

Fig. 55

Now release $P$ and $J$, and join the clips of $P$ and $K$. The bulb will still be *off*. It is just as if transistor $T_1$ had *two* seperate inputs, $J$ and $K$. If either of these are at a high voltage, the bulb will be *off*.

Touch the clip of $J$ onto the positive line. The bulb will stay *off*.

Touch the clip of $J$ onto the negative line, and the bulb is still *off*.

So long as transistor $T_1$ can get its base current from its $K$ input, it does not respond to its $J$ input.

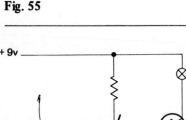

Fig. 56

Now release $P$ and $K$, and join $N$ and $K$. The bulb will be *on*.
Touch $J$ onto the negative line and the bulb will be *on*.
Touch $J$ onto the positive line and the bulb will go *off*.

The transistor $T_1$ *is now responding* to its $J$ input.
We can summarize this as:
If the $K$ input is high, the $J$ input has no effect.
If the $K$ input is low, the $J$ input does have an effect.

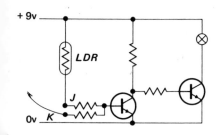

This is called a *gate*. We could use it like the circuit of Fig. 57.

If $K$ is at a low voltage, then the circuit responds to whether it is light or dark. The gate is *open* between the *L.D.R.* and the bulb.

If $K$ is at a high voltage, then the circuit does not respond to the *L.D.R.* The gate is *closed*.

   In the computer we describe in Chapter 11, *Computer Circuits*, (see page 52), we shall make use of this gate.

**Fig. 57**

# 5 More Switching Circuits

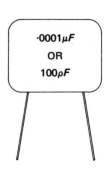

**Fig. 58**

We have just been looking at one sort of *switch*, called a *bistable switch*, because it will stay in either of two positions. An electric light switch is like this, since it will stay *off* or *on*, depending on whether it is switched up or down. But there are other sorts of switches.

A front-door bell is worked from a switch that is normally *off*. If someone presses the switch is comes *on* and the bell rings. If the person releases the switch the bell stops ringing. This is an example of a switch that is stable only in *one* position (the *off* position) and has to be held down, if we want it to go into the other position. When released it returns to its one stable position. Such a switch is called a *mono-stable switch*.

To make this switch with transistors, we use a component called a *Capacitor*. This is a picture of a capacitor.

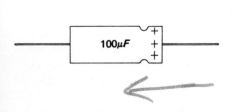

**Fig. 59**

This is a picture of a large capacitor, which is called an *electrolytic capacitor*.

The capacitor is a component which is used to *store* electricity. If we connect a capacitor to a battery, electric current will flow into the capacitor until it is full. (This is rather like water flowing into the water cistern of a lavatory. When the cistern is full, a valve closes and the water stops flowing in).

The amount of electricity that the capacitor can hold is called its *capacitance*. This is measured in *microfarads* (symbol $\mu$ F). (Sometimes very small capacitances are measured in *picofarads* (pF). 1 000 000 picofarads are equal to 1 microfarad). The bigger the capacitance, the more electricity the capacitor can store.

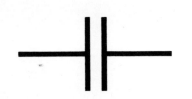

**Fig. 60**

Small capacitors (usually having a capacitance less than 1 $\mu$ F) are able to withstand high voltages, and they can be connected into a circuit either way round.

This is the circuit symbol for this sort of capacitor.

**Fig. 61**

Electrolytic capacitors (usually greater than $1\,\mu F$) are made in a special way, so that they do not become too bulky. Because of this they can only withstand small voltages, and they must be connected into the circuit with their positive leads connected towards the more positive side of the circuit, and their negative leads to the negative side.

This is the circuit symbol for the electrolytic capacitor.

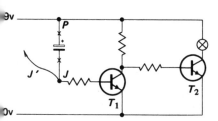

**Fig. 62**

Return to the circuit of Fig. 47. Now connect a $100\,\mu F$ capacitor between leads $P$ and $J$ as in the diagram of Fig. 62. Make sure that the positive end of the capacitor goes to clip $P$, and the negative end goes to clip $J$.

When the battery is reconnected, current will flow into the capacitor. Whilst it does this there will be a base current, and transistor $T_1$ will be turned *on*. Thus transistor $T_2$ will be *off* and the bulb will be *off*.

When the capacitor is full of electricty (we say *fully charged*), the current stops flowing and transistor $T_1$ is turned *off*. So transistor $T_2$ and the bulb will be turned *on*.

To do this again, we must empty the electicity from the capacitor (we say *discharge* the capacitor). (This is like 'pulling the chain' of the water cistern!) This is done by touching the clip of lead $J$ ' onto the positive line, which provides a *short circuit* across the capacitor and discharges it.

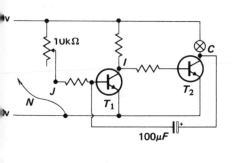

**Fig. 63**

We can make this circuit into a *mono-stable switch* as follows;

Solder the $100\,\mu F$ capacitor into the circuit as shown. Use plastic covered wire to make the connections to the collector of transistor $T_2$ and the base of transistor $T_1$, otherwise the wires might touch other parts of the circuit. Make sure that you get the capacitor the right way round. Clip the variable resistor between leads $P$ and $J$.

If the clip of lead $N$ is touched onto the collector of $T_2$ (pin $C$), the bulb will come *on*, remain *on* for several seconds and then go *off* again.

We can vary the time that the bulb is *on* by adjusting the variable resistor.

The most important use of this mono-stable switch is as a *time-switch*. It will measure an interval of time, during which the bulb is *on*.

Initially, after touching the collector of $T_2$ (pin $C$) with the clip of lead $N$, the capacitor is discharged, so $C$ and $J$ are at a low voltage and the bulb is *on*.

Current flows through the variable resistor to charge up the capacitor, so the voltage at the base of $T_1$ rises until it is large enough to switch transistor $T_1$ *on*. Transistor $T_2$ and the bulb are turned *off*.

The bigger the resistance of the variable resistor, the smaller is the current to the capacitor, so the longer it takes to charge up, so the bulb remains *on* longer.

In Chapter 10 *Electronic Projects,* (see page 42) a more useful form of time switch is described.

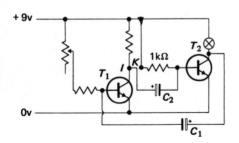

+ 9v

0v

$T_1$ $I$ $K$ $1k\Omega$ $T_2$

$C_2$

$C_1$

**Fig. 64**

Unsolder the 1 k$\Omega$ resistor from pin $I$ and resolder it onto another brass pin $K$ as in the diagram. Solder a flying lead with crocodile clip onto this pin $K$ and then attach the clip to the positive line.

Solder another 100 $\mu F$ capacitor between pin $I$ and the base of transistor $T_2$. (Make sure that the positive end of the capacitor goes to pin $I$).

When the battery is reconnected the bulb will switch alternately *on* and *off*. The 'speed' at which it switches *on* and *off* is called its *frequency*. This frequency can be changed by adjusting the variable resistor.

This is called an *astable switch*, because it does not settle into one position, but continuously changes from one state to the other.

Suppose that initially transistor $T_1$ is *off* and $T_2$ is *on*, so that the bulb is *on* also. The base of $T_1$ is at a *low* voltage. Capacitor $C_1$ is charged up by the current flowing through the variable resistor, and when the voltage at the base of $T_1$ becomes high enough, $T_1$ switches *on* which brings the collector of $T_1$ to a *low* voltage. This immediately brings the other side of capacitor $C_2$, and hence the base of $T_2$, to a low voltage, and $T_2$ switches *off*. $C_2$ now charges up until the base of $T_2$ is high enough, and then $T_2$ switches *on* causing the base of $T_1$ to go to a *low* voltage once again. The process thus continues.

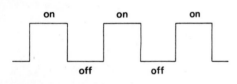

on    on    on

off    off

**Fig. 65**

The trouble with this simple astable switch is that we can only adjust the rate at which capacitor $C_1$ charges up, capacitor $C_2$ always charges at a constant rate through the 1 k$\Omega$ resistor.

The switching process can be described by this zig-zag line. The upper part of the line represents the time that the bulb is *on*, while the bottom part represents the time that it is *off*.

In this diagram the bulb is *on* for the same length of time that it is *off*. We say it has an *equal mark/space ratio*.

**Fig. 66**

We can also show the *frequency* at which the bulb switches *on* and *off*, by making the *on* times and the *off* times much shorter or longer. This represents a higher frequency . . .

**Fig. 67**

. . . while this represents a lower frequency. Notice that in all these cases the mark/space ratio is the same, even though the frequencies are different.

This represents a situation where the bulb is *on* for a *longer* time than it is *off*, or as we say a *high mark/space* ratio . . .

**Fig. 68**

. . . whereas this represents a situation where the bulb is *on* for a *shorter* time than it is *off*, (a *low mark/space* ratio).

Notice that in both these cases the number of times that the bulb flashes every minute still remains the same, (the *frequencies* are equal).

**Fig. 69**

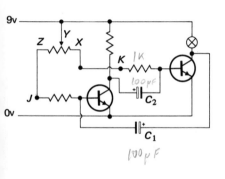

**Fig. 70**

The simple circuit of Fig. 64 alters both the *mark/space* ratio *and* the frequency, when the variable resistor is adjusted. In order to get a circuit where the *mark/space* ratio can be altered without changing the frequency, we need to connect the variable resistor to both capacitors.

Release the clip of lead $K$ from the positive line and clip it onto terminal $X$ of the variable resistor (see Fig. 15).

Make sure that the clip of lead $P$ goes to the $Y$ terminal of the variable resistor, and the clip of lead $J$ goes to the $Z$ terminal.

When the variable resistor is turned fully clockwise, capacitor $C_2$ is charged through the 1 k$\Omega$ resistor (quickly) whereas capacitor $C_1$ is charged through the full 10 k$\Omega$ of the variable resistor plus the 10 k$\Omega$ fixed resistor (slowly). Thus the bulb remains *on* for longer than it is *off* (a *high mark/space* ratio).

When the variable resistor is turned fully anti-clockwise, it is capacitor $C_2$ that is charged through the full 10 k$\Omega$ of the variable resistor. This leads to a *low mark/space* ratio.

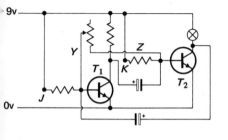

**Fig. 71**

This circuit will alter the frequency without changing the *mark/space* ratio, because instead of taking resistance from one capacitor and giving it to the other (as above), it takes resistance from *both* capacitors at once.

To make up this circuit remove the variable resistor and solder two plastic covered wire leads onto terminals $Y$ and $Z$. Solder the terminal $Y$ lead to the base of transistor $T_1$ and the $Z$ lead to the base of transistor $T_2$. By altering the variable resistor, you can now alter the speed at which the light flashes over a large range. (If the variable resistor is turned fully anti-clockwise, the circuit may stop working. To get it going again, turn the variable resistor fully clockwise, disconnect the battery and then reconnect it again.)

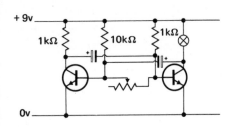

The circuit diagram shown in Fig. 72 is identical to that of Fig. 71. It has been re-arranged so that we do not have so many wires crossing over one another in the circuit diagram. Do not make up this circuit, since you already have it! We have drawn it like this, because this is the way we want to draw the circuits in Chapter 11, *Computer Circuits*.

**Fig. 72**

We now want to listen to the electric currents as they switch on and off in the transistors. We do this with the earpiece. This is a device that turns electric currents into sound. So that it can be soldered into the circuit, cut off the plug at the end of the twisted leads, separate the leads a little, and remove some of the plastic covering from the leads.

**Fig. 73**

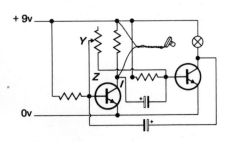

Solder the earpiece across the 1 kΩ resistor as in the diagram. One lead goes to pin *I*, while the other goes to the positive line. When the battery is re-connected, it should be possible to hear a series of clicks in the earpiece, that correspond to the voltage at pin *I* going *high* and *low* alternately as the bulb goes *on* and *off*. By adjusting the variable resistor you can alter the frequency of the clicks so that they come faster or slower.

**Fig. 74**

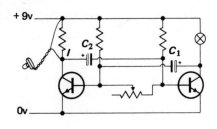

By using smaller capacitors that charge up quicker, we can make the clicks come faster.

Remove the capacitor $C_1$ and replace it with a $2\,\mu F$ capacitor. (Work out for yourself which way round it has to go)

The clicks in the earpiece will be very much faster, and the bulb will flicker *on* and *off* very fast.

**Fig. 75**

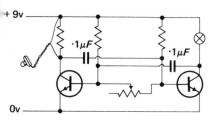

By using still smaller capacitors, the frequency of the clicks can be increased still further, so that they sound like a continuous note.

Remove both capacitors and replace them with the $0.1\,\mu F$ capacitors. (These are not electrolytic capacitors, so they can be connected either way round)

The frequency of the note will be about 1 000 clicks every second (which we say is 1 000 *hertz* or Hz for short). This frequency can be altered with the variable resistor.

A circuit which produces a rapid change in the electric currents like this is called an *oscillator* (because it *oscillates*). We use an oscillator like this to make an electronic organ, like the one described in Chapter 10, *Electronic Projects.*

**Fig. 76**

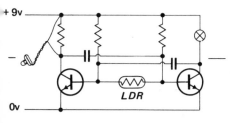

We could replace the variable resistor by the light dependent resistor, so that the frequency of the oscillator depends upon the amount of light falling on the *L.D.R.* —a sort of light sensitive oscillator.

Also by replacing the variable resistor with the thermistor instead, we could even make a temperature sensitive oscillator. Perhaps you can think up some more uses of this circuit!

Because it is so useful it has several names, which you will find in some other books on electronics. It is sometimes called a *multivibrator*, or a *flip-flop.*

**Fig. 77**

We have now come to an end of the switching circuits of the transistor. You can now go on to build some of the circuits described in Chapter 11, *Computer Circuits* (see page 52). Alternatively, you can go on to some of the projects in Chapter 10 on page 42, but you will find it useful to read Chapter 9, *Electro-magnetic Relays,* (see page 39) before starting the projects. Finally you can go onto the amplifier and radio circuits of the next chapters.

Whichever you do, first clear all the components and pins from the soft-board. Unsolder the transistors, but remove capacitors and resistors by cutting the wires as close to the pins as possible. Remove the bulb holder and all pins from the board also.

# 6 Alternating Currents

Do you remember this circuit? The bulb lights up because electric current from the battery flows round the circuit from the positive pole to the negative pole.

How fast does the electricity travel?

You will be surprised to know that any single 'piece' of electricity may take several *hours* to get from the battery to the bulb!

Why, then, does the bulb light up as soon as the battery is connected?

**Fig. 78**

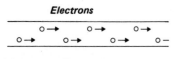

*Electrons*

*Piece of wire*

We call the 'pieces' of electricity *'electrons'*. '

At the moment the battery is connected, the electrons near the battery are given a little push. These electrons push the ones next to them and so on until the 'push' travels right round the circuit, and this happens very quickly indeed.

The same happens with the water in the tap. The moment you turn on the tap, the water appears, but any particular 'bit' of water may take several *days* to get from the reservoir to the tap.

**Fig. 79**

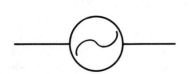

Most of the electric currents we have been using up till now have been *direct currents,* which flow in one direction only. But do you remember the circuit (Fig. 76), which gave a whistling noise in the earpiece?

It does this because the electric current 'sloshes' backwards and forwards in the earpiece, as the voltage across the transistor goes alternately high and low. This sort of electricity is called *alternating current,* and it is made by an *oscillator.* This is the symbol for an oscillator.

**Fig. 80**

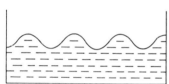
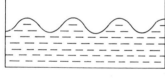

In order to see what alternating currents will do, half-fill a sink, or rectangular bowl with water.

If you place your hand in the water and give it a quick sideways push, a wave will travel down to the end of the sink, (where it might be reflected).

If you move your hand slowly backwards and forwards, a succession of waves will travel down to the end of the sink. This is how alternating currents travel down a wire.

Now move your hand backwards and forwards very fast (or as we say, at a high frequency), the waves will be closer together, but they will still move at the same speed.

If you can get your hand moving at just the right speed, the size of the waves increases, until the water slops over the end of the sink. We say that we are at the *resonant* frequency.

**Fig. 81**

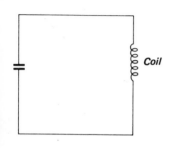

Coil

It is possible to make an electric circuit which has a resonant frequency like this; where the electric current is small except at one particular frequency (the resonant freqeuency).

We call this sort of circuit a *resonant circuit*, and we use it to separate one frequency from another.

The diagram shows a simple resonant circuit used in a radio set. It consists of a capacitor and a coil of wire.

**Fig. 82**

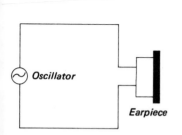

Oscillator

Earpiece

Alternating currents are needed to make sounds, speech and music.

This diagram shows an oscillator (which makes alternating currents) connected to an earpiece. If the alternating current were to go backwards and forwards about 200 times every second, (or, as we say, at 200 Hz), we would hear a low-pitched note in the earpiece.

If we increased the frequency to 1 000 Hz (or 1 kHz) the pitch of the note would be much higher. If we could look inside the wires of a radio set, which is playing music, we would see lots of these alternating currents of many different frequencies, which correspond to the frequencies of the notes being played by the musicians.

**Fig. 83**

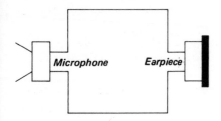

The instrument used to turn musical sounds into these alternating currents is called a *microphone*.

The alternating currents then travel along the wires to the loud-speaker or earpiece, as in the diagram.

However, the electric currents would be far too small to make the earpiece work properly, so with this simple arrangement you would not hear very much.

**Fig. 84**

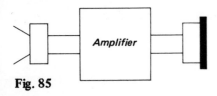

To make the output from the earpiece loud enough, we put an *amplifier* in the circuit to amplify the alternating currents.

We shall see how to make an amplifier in the next chapter. We make it with the transistor that we have been using already to make our switching circuits more sensitive.

**Fig. 85**

# 7 An Amplifier

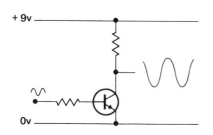

**Fig. 86**

The most important part of our amplifier is the transistor. Do you remember how it works?

Small changes in the base current become large changes in the current through the transistor, and this causes large changes in the voltage at the collector of the transistor.

Imagine what would happen if you were jumping up and down on a trampoline, which was placed only a short distance from the ground. You would be continually hitting your feet on the ground. On the other hand, if the trampoline were placed very high up, near to the roof, you would be continually hitting your head on the ceiling! The best place for the trampoline is somewhere near the middle of the room.

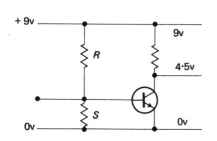

**Fig. 87**

It is the same with the transistor. We want the voltage at the collector to swing up and down by equal amounts. We therefore want to set the collector voltage about half-way between the positive line voltage (9 volts) and the negative line voltage (0 volts), or somewhere between 4 and 5 volts.

This is known as *biasing* the transistor.

We do this by choosing just the right values of $R$ and $S$ in the diagram, so that the transistor is neither switched *on* nor *off*, but somewhere in between.

Notice that we no longer put a resistor between $R$ and $S$ and the base of the transistor. This is to make our amplifier even more sensitive.

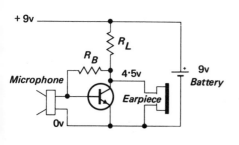

**Fig. 88**

The actual values we use for $R$ and $S$ may vary, depending upon how good our transistor is. For this reason we prefer to bias the transistor in a different way, as in the circuit diagram. Only one biasing resistor is used, and this has a resistance of about 100 times that of the *load* resistor, (the one connected between the positive line and the collector, labelled $R_L$).

To use this amplifier, we connect the microphone across the negative line and the base, and we connect the earpiece across the negative line and the collector, as in the diagram.

Starting in the centre of the soft-board, push pins into the board as in the diagram. The components will be soldered onto these pins.

Do this in the following order;
connecting wire and battery clip first, then resistors and the earpiece and finally the transistor.

Take another earpiece and cut the plug from the end. Separate the twisted leads a little, remove about 0·5 cm of the plastic from each lead and solder them across the base of the transistor and the negative line. This will act as the microphone.

Attach the battery and plug the earpiece (the one on the right) into your ear. By blowing into the microphone, you should hear a rustling sound in the earpiece.

If you get a friend to speak into the microphone, you might just be able to hear him in the earpiece, but it will not be very loud. We obviously need *more* amplification.

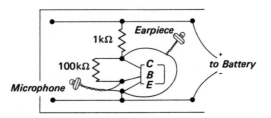

**Fig. 89**

We cannot just feed the output from the collector of one transistor straight into the base of a second transistor. This is because they are at different voltages, and we would upset the biasing if we did it like this.

We need a component which will allow the alternating currents to pass through, whilst keeping the biasing voltages apart. This is what the capacitor does in this circuit.

Notice that the capacitor is connected with its positive end to the collector of the first transistor, and its negative end to the base of the second transistor.

The second transistor will now amplify the output from the first transistor to give an even bigger sound in the earpiece.

Because we want to use the left side of the soft-board for our radio set, build this new transistor *stage* after the first *stage*. You will have to remove the earpiece and solder it back into its new position later.

Attach the battery and plug the earpiece into your ear. Blow into the microphone, or get a friend to speak into it, and you should hear a very much louder sound in the earpiece. This shows that the second transistor has increased the overall amplification.

The addition of a third transistor stage will increase this still further.

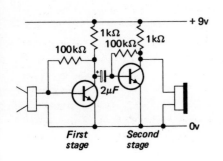

**Fig. 90**

Solder in the third transistor stage after the second stage. Again you will have to remove the earpiece and solder it into its new position later.

Once more test the overall amplification of the amplifier by getting a friend to speak into the microphone.

If you get funny noises in the earpiece, like bumping noises or whistles, this is because you now have too much amplification. Continue with the next section and the trouble may correct itself.

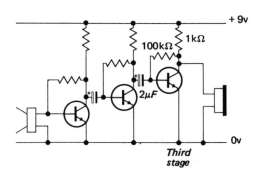

**Fig. 91**

The addition of this third stage might make the sound in the earpiece *too* loud, so we shall also add a *loudness control*, (often called a *volume* control). This is just the variable resistor we used before. Solder the variable resistor onto three brass pins stuck into the softboard between stages one and two, as in the diagram. Another 2μF capacitor (C) is placed between the Y terminal of the variable resistor and the base of the following transistor. Note which way round this capacitor is placed:

The output from the first transistor stage is fed to the variable resistor across terminals $X$ and $Z$. When the variable resistor is turned fully clockwise, the sliding contact $Y$ is close to terminal $X$, so that all the alternating current from the first stage gets to the second and third stages and we have maximum loudness. When the variable resistor is turned more and more anti-clockwise, more and more resistance is introduced between $Y$ and $X$, so the alternating current to the second and third stages is reduced, and we have less loudness. We can thus control the loudness with the variable resistor.

A project to turn this simple amplifier into an *intercom* for speaking over large distances in either direction is given in Chapter 10, *Electronic Projects* (see page 42).

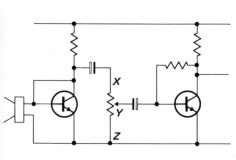

**Fig. 92**

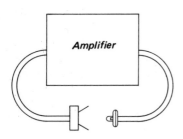

**Fig. 93**

You may notice that if the variable resistor is turned fully clockwise, there are queer noises in the earpiece. This is due to *feedback*.

Alternating currents in the third stage of the amplifier get back along the positive line to the earlier stages, where they are amplified again, and passed on to the third stage. Here they are amplified and passed back again. Eventually these alternating currents go round and round the amplifier, producing a noise in the earpiece, regardless of whether there is a microphone or not.

The amplifier has become an oscillator.

One way of producing these oscillations is by *acoustic* feedback. Hold the earpiece as close as possible to the microphone, and turn the loudness control to maximum. The earpiece should make a high-pitched whistling noise, which is the alternating current in the earpiece being turned into sound, which is picked up by the microphone and turned back into alternating current. This is amplified and passed on to the earpiece, and so the process continues.

You may have been in a hall, where this has happened because someone turned up the loudspeaker system too much.

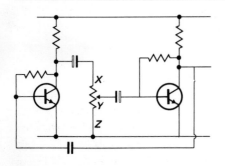

**Fig. 94**

Another way of producing these oscillations is by electrical feedback. We take some of the output voltage and feed it back to an earlier stage through a capacitor. The amplifier then becomes an oscillator.

Solder a $0.01\,\mu F$ capacitor as in the diagram. When the battery is reconnected, the earpiece should emit a loud whistle, which can be controlled by the variable resistor.

This is not a very good way of making an oscillator, but it does show how it can be done. Now go back and look at Fig. 74. This also is an oscillator, and you should be able to see that it is very similar to Fig. 94.

# 8 A Radio Receiver

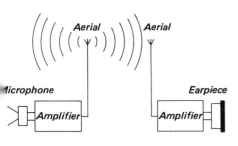

**Fig. 95**

Suppose that instead of connecting the amplifier to an earpiece we connect it to a piece of wire sticking up into the air (which is called an *aerial*). When someone speaks into the microphone, the alternating currents would be amplified and passed on to this aerial, where they would spread out into the room as an *electro-magnetic wave*. This is just like the waves that spread out when a stone is dropped into a pond.

If we had another aerial set up a short distance away, connected to the *input* of another amplifier having an earpiece but no microphone, we would be able to pick up these electro-magnetic waves and turn them back into sound at the earpiece. We would have transmitted the original speech through space as an electro-magnetic wave. This is *not* a sound wave because it can travel through a vacuum.

Audio frequency signal

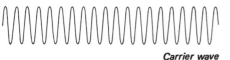

Carrier wave

Modulated carrier wave

The frequency of this electro-magnetic wave would be about 500 Hz. It would only travel for a very short distance. If we could increase the frequency to about 1 000 000 Hz (or 1 Megahertz, 1 MHz) the electro-magnetic wave could travel for *hundreds of miles*. Unfortunately if such an electro-magnetic wave were then picked up by an aerial and turned back into sound, we would not be able to hear anything. This is because the highest note that a human ear can hear is about 15 000 Hz (15 kHz).

This is the problem that radio inventors have to solve.

The frequencies of sound, speech and music (called *audio* frequencies) have an electro-magnetic wave which does not travel very far.

Frequencies of about 1 MHz travel much better, but cannot be heard when they are turned back into sound.

They solve this problem in a very clever way. First of all they use an electro-magnetic wave of about 1 MHz (called a *carrier* wave), which they turn on and off at the frequency of the speech or music. This is called *modulating the carrier wave*. Then they *transmit* this modulated carrier wave through space. A *receiver* picks up this modulated carrier wave and separates out the audio frequencies (the speech or music). This is called *de-modulating*.

They then amplify the audio frequencies and put them into the earpiece.

The diagram shows the carrier wave, the modulated carrier wave and the audio frequency used to modualte it.

**Fig. 96**

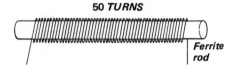

50 *TURNS*

*Ferrite rod*

**Fig. 97**

We shall see later how to make a radio transmitter. For the moment we shall make a radio receiver to pick up the broadcasting stations which are already transmitting.

Any radio receiver must do three things. It must be able to separate one broadcasting station from another, (this is called *tuning*). It must separate the audio frequencies from the carrier wave (called *de-modulating*). It must amplify these audio frequencies.

We already have an amplifier to do this third job, so we shall first make a circuit to do the *tuning* and then one to do the *de-modulating*.

Take the *ferrite rod* and wind onto it 50 turns of plastic-covered wire. Keep the turns close together and wind them all in the same direction. Secure the turns with tape.

(Be careful not to drop the ferrite rod or it may break. If this does happen it will still work if it is stuck together with strong glue).

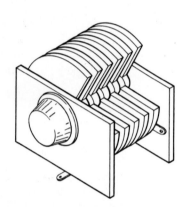

**Fig. 98**

Now take the variable capacitor (shown in the diagram). This has two sets of plates which do not touch, but which can be slid over each other to alter their capacitance. For the variable capacitor we are using, the capacitance can be changed from about 50 p$F$ to about 500 p$F$.

Fix a knob to the variable capacitor and solder it to two brass pins stuck into the extreme left hand side of the soft-board about half way down, as in the next diagram (Fig. 99).

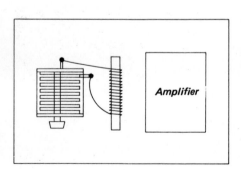

*Amplifier*

**Fig. 99**

Solder the ends of the ferrite rod coil of wire onto these pins as in the diagram. This forms the *tuning circuit*.

The electro-magnetic waves sent out by all the broadcasting stations in the world are picked up by the ferrite rod, which acts as the aerial. These cause alternating currents to go round the circuit from the ferrite rod coil to the variable capacitor and back again, just like the water sloshing up and down the sink as described in Fig. 81.

Do you remember what a *resonant* frequency is? This is the frequency which is just right for the water in the sink, so that the waves of water slop over the sides of the sink.

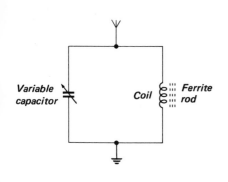

Variable capacitor    Coil    Ferrite rod

The same thing happens with our resonant circuit here. (Note that we are now using the circuit symbols for the variable capacitor and the ferrite rod coil).

Each broadcasting station uses a different carrier wave, which is shown by its *wave-length*. These carrier waves all have a different frequency. Thus the BBC Radio One programme is broadcast on 247 metres wavelength (a frequency of 1·2 MHz), while Radio Three is on 464 metres (650 kHz).

When we adjust the variable capacitor (called *tuning*), we alter the frequency at which the circuit will resonate. Suppone we alter it so that 650 kHz becomes the resonant frequency. Then the carrier wave of the Radio Three programme will have just the right frequency for this circuit.

The alternating currents in the circuit will build up to a very large value, so we shall be able to use them and listen in to the Radio Three broadcast.

We do not need to *know* what frequency to tune to. All we do is turn the variable capacitor slowly, until we hear the station required. (In some parts of the country Radio Three is on a different frequency, so the setting of the variable capacitor will be different. Our tuning circuit will pick up all broadcasting stations between 200 metres to 500 metres, which is called the *Medium wave band*).

**Fig. 100**

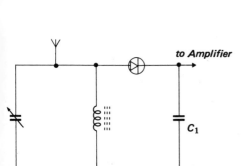

to Amplifier

$C_1$

to Amplifier

We must now have a de-modulating circuit to separate the speech and music from the carrier wave.

In its simplest form this is just a diode. Do you remember how it works? Go back to Fig. 19.

The diode allows current to flow through it in one direction, but not the opposite direction.

If we fed an alternating current into a capacitor directly, it would firstly charge up one way round and then discharge and then charge up the opposite way round.

If we use the circuit of Fig. 101, the capacitor will charge up one way round (in the forward direction of the diode), but it will not be able to charge up the opposite way round, since the diode will not let the current go through it in the reverse direction. The capacitor would receive a series of 'pushes' all in the same direction, and these pushes would be stronger for a large alternating current and smaller for a small alternating current. But our alternating current comes from a carrier wave, which has been modulated with an audio frequency, so that it is continually getting larger and smaller.

The voltage across the capacitor $C_1$ thus follows the audio frequency.

**Fig. 101**

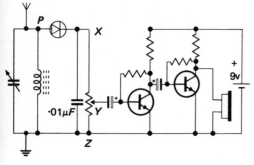

**Fig. 102**

We finally feed the voltages from this capacitor into the amplifier we have already built.

First remove the first stage of the amplifier (or it will be too sensitive and may produce oscillations). Connect a $0.01\ \mu F$ capacitor across the variable resistor, and solder a lead to join the bottom of the tuning circuit to the terminal $Z$ of the variable resistor. Solder the diode between a pin $P$ stuck into the board as shown and the terminal $X$ of the variable resistor. Connect pin $P$ and the top of the tuning circuit with a lead.

Now reconnect the battery. You should be able to hear something in the earpiece if you slowly turn the variable capacitor back and forth. (The loudness control should be turned up to maximum loudness).

In some areas of the country, it may be difficult to get more than one station. This is because the other broadcasting stations are too far away. This will be corrected by adding another stage. In same areas too, one station may be so strong that it blocks out all the others. We shall correct this by making our tuning circuit more *selective*, so that it separates the different stations better.

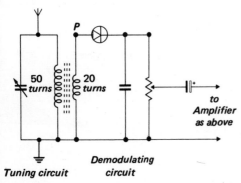

Tuning circuit     Demodulating circuit

**Fig. 103**

Remove the lead between the tuning circuit and pin $P$. Remove the ferrite rod and its coil. Wind *another* coil of wire *on top of* the existing 50 turn coil, and make the new coil of 20 turns. Again secure the turns with tape.

Replace the ferrite rod and its coils, with the leads of the 50 turn coil going to the variable capacitor exactly as before. Solder one end of the 20 turn coil to pin $P$ and the other end to the negative line.

When the battery is reconnected you should find that the broadcasting stations are now easier to separate, but the sound they produce is much weaker.

This is because we have partly separated the tuning circuit from the de-modulating circuit. The tuning circuit works better, but only passes on a very small alternating current to the diode. In order to increase these alternating currents we use another transistor amplifying stage.

The complete radio receiver is shown here, together with the new stage added. By now you should be able to work out where to put the pins.

Notice that we have three components in the circuit which are not there for an obvious purpose. You should know by now the purpose of the resistor labelled $R_L$ and the resistor labelled $R_B$. But what about $C_1, C_2$ and $R_3$?

The capacitor $C_2$ does the same as the capacitors in the amplifier, it stops the voltage at the collector of the transistor from upsetting the bias on the next stage. In this case it stops the collector voltage from upsetting the way the diode works. The alternating currents from the tuning circuit can get through the capacitor $C_2$ to the diode, but the direct currents from the battery cannot do so.

The capacitor $C_1$ does the same. If the bottom end of the 20 turn coil were connected directly to the negative line, the bias on the transistor would be upset. Capacitor $C_1$ enables the alternating currents to get to the negative line, but stops the direct currents from doing so.

The resistor $R_3$ is to prevent capacitor $C_2$ from charging up too much. Capacitor $C_2$ is likely to charge up because of the diode action as we explained in Fig. 101. To provide a discharge path for $C_2$ we put in resistor $R_3$. (Those who are really clever will see that the variable resistor also provides a discharge path for the capacitor $C_4$. We want the capacitor to charge up *a little* so that it will demodulate the carrier wave, but not *too much* or it will stop the audio frequencies as well).

When you have completed this circuit, you should be able to get several broadcasting stations with it. If you can you will have done well. If you can go through the circuit, pointing to each component and saying what it is for, you will have done even better. After all this book is to help you to understand how a radio set works, not just to tell you how to make it.

If you find that the receiver tends to whistle or oscillate, try swapping over the ends of the 20 turn coil. This should reduce the un-wanted feedback and stop the oscillations.

This completes our study of radio receivers and amplifiers. You can go on to Chapter 10 *Electronic Projects*, if you want a bit more. There you will find details of a simple radio transmitter.

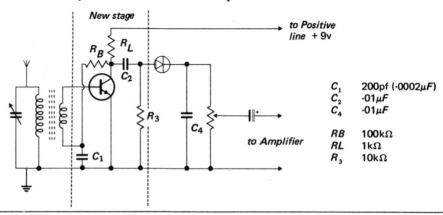

Fig. 104

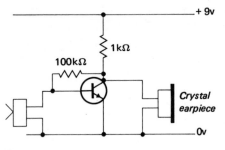

**Fig. A**

## Special note: Loudspeakers and Magnetic Earpieces

So far we have used a *crystal* earpiece to listen to the sounds produced by an oscillator, amplifier or radio receiver. We just connected the earpiece across the transistor between the collector and the emitter. Since the crystal earpiece has a very high resistance (about 10 MΩ), it only takes a tiny current, and so it does not upset the working of the transistor.

If we were to use a *magnetic* earpiece (resistance of about 1 kΩ) or a loudspeaker (resistance about 100Ω) in the same way, the working of the transistor *would* be upset, and there would not be any sound produced.

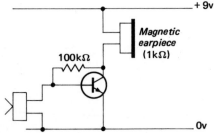

**Fig. B**

The correct way to use low resistance devices like these is to put them into the circuit *in place of* the load resistor (see Fig. 88).

In the case of the magnetic earpiece, which has the same resistance as the load resistor it is replacing, we do not need to alter anything else. The circuit will be like Fig. *B* instead of like Fig. 88. The same change will apply to Fig. 90, 91 and 92.

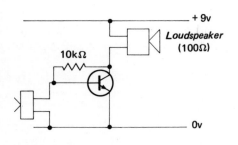

Fig. C

If, however, we use a loudspeaker or a magnetic earpiece with a smaller resistance (say about 100Ω), the bias resistor will have to be much smaller, about 10 kΩ, as in the diagram.

Loudspeakers and magnetic earpieces with even smaller resistance, cannot be used like this with the sort of transistors we have, because they would have to carry too much current and would be damaged. Instead, bigger transistors called *power* transistors have to be used. For the simple circuits we have been looking at, it is easier to use a crystal earpiece.

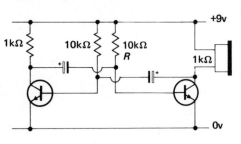

**Fig. D**

In astable switching circuits, we are not interested in correctly biasing the transistor, so we put the magnetic earpiece or loudspeaker into the circuit in place of the bulb, as in Fig. *D*. If the device has the same resistance as the bulb (100Ω) then nothing else in the circuit will be changed, all the other components will be the same as for Fig. 75.

If, however, the earpiece has a higher resistance (say 1 kΩ), we alter the value of the resistor *R* to 10 kΩ, as shown.

Several of the projects in chapter 10 use a loudspeaker (resistance 75Ω) in the way described above.

# 9 The Electro-magnetic Relay

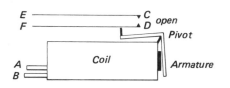

**Fig. 105**

This is a picture of an electro-magnetic relay. It is made from a coil of wire wound around a soft-iron core, with the ends of this coil at the terminals $A$ and $B$.

When a battery is connected across $A$ and $B$, the soft-iron core becomes a magnet and attracts the *armature* (shown on the diagram). When this happens, we say the relay is 'energised' or simply that it is *on*.

When the battery is disconnected, the soft-iron core ceases to be a magnet and the armature is 'released', or as we say, the relay is *off*.

Solder flexible leads to the terminals $A$ and $B$, and watch the relay come *on* and go *off* as the battery is connected and then disconnected to these leads.

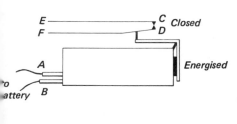

**Fig. 106**

When the armature moves, it opens and closes a set of *contacts* (marked $C$ and $D$). These contacts are connected to terminals $E$ and $F$ as in the diagram.

When the relay is *on*, contacts $C$ and $D$ are closed, and an electric current can pass through the terminals $E$ and $F$.

When the relay is *off* the contacts open, and no current can pass through the terminals $E$ and $F$.

We can think of this as a switch, that can be opened or closed by a voltage across the coil terminals $A$ and $B$. When this voltage is high, the relay is *on*, and the switch is closed.

When the voltage across $A$ and $B$ is low, the relay is *off* and the switch is open, as in Fig. 105.

Fig. 106 shows the relay in the *on* position.

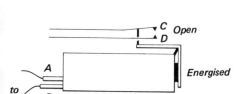

**Fig. 107**

Sometimes the contacts $C$ and $D$ are *closed* when the relay is *off*, and open when it is *on*. This is the opposite of the relay of Fig. 105.

In order to know which are which we say that the contacts which are like Fig. 105 are *normally open* contacts (because they are open when the relay is *off*).

The contacts which behave like Fig. 107 are called *normally closed* contacts (because they are closed when the relay is *off*).

Can you identify the two different types of contact on your relay?

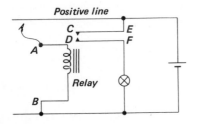

This is the circuit diagram of a relay and its contacts.

It is not possible to pass a large current through transistors like the ones we have been using. So it is not possible for a simple transistor switch to be used to switch on a powerful light, or electric bell or electric motor.

If the small current from a transistor is used to switch a relay *on*, then we can use the relay contacts to switch on a very much larger current.

Try this simple circuit. When the flying lead *A* is connected to the positive line, the relay pulls in the armature and the normally open contacts *C* and *D* close. The bulb circuit, which is connected to *C* and *D* through the terminals *E* and *F*, is thus switched *on*, and the bulb comes on. (Notice that we have used the same battery to light the bulb as we used to energise the relay. We could have used a different battery).

**Fig. 108**

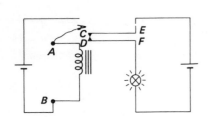

In this circuit we are using the normally closed contacts, so that the bulb is normally *on*, but goes *off* when the relay is energised by touching lead *A* onto the positive line.

(Notice that we are using a separate battery for the bulb this time, to show you how to do it. We could have used the same battery for the bulb and the relay. Can you work out how to do it?)

**Fig. 109**

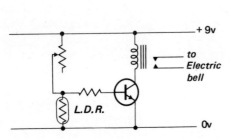

This is how we connect the relay to the transistor. We just put it in place of the bulb.

This is just the switching circuit of Fig. 43. The relay is *off* when a light is shining onto the *L.D.R.* If the light is cut off (by a burglar who passes in front of the *L.D.R.*!), the relay comes *on*. If we have an electric bell connected to the normally open contacts, together with a suitable battery, the bell will ring (and scare off the burglar).

**Fig. 110**

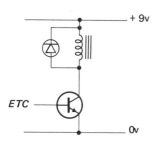

The trouble with the simple relay connections of Fig. 110 is that when the relay is switched off, a very large voltage called a *back-voltage*, is produced in the relay. This may be enough to damage the transistor.

To stop this, a diode is connected across the relay as shown. The battery voltage is applied in the reverse direction so that no current normally flows through this diode. When, however, the relay switches *off*, the large back-voltage produced is the opposite way to the battery voltage, so it *can* go through the diode. The transistor is thus protected from the back-voltage.

Whenever a relay is switched on or off with a transistor, a diode must be used in this way.

**Fig. 111**

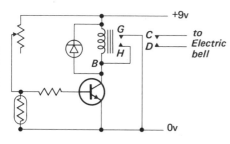

There is also another fault with the simple circuit of Fig. 110. When the burglar has passed right in front of the *L.D.R.* so that light falls on it once again, the relay will go *off* and the bell will stop ringing.

In order to make it so that the bell continues to ring, even when the burglar has moved on, we connect the relay as a *self-holding* relay. This is done with the other set of normally open contacts, which are connected as in the diagram. Normally the relay is *off*, so no current can get to terminal *B* via the contacts *G* and *H*.

When the burglar operates the relay by passing in front of the *L.D.R.* the relay pulls up for a short time. The contacts *G* and *H* close, and current can then get through to the relay, bypassing the transistor. The relay will thus remain *on*, even when the burglar has moved on and the transistor is again in the *off* position.

We use a self-holding relay like this whenever we want to *trigger* a circuit, which then remains in the *on* position. This is very much like the bistable circuit described in Fig. 52.

**Fig. 112**

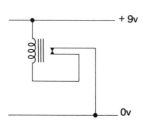

The other use of the relay is described in this circuit. The normally closed contacts are used with the coil terminals so that when the battery is connected the relay pulls in the armature. The normally closed contacts then open, and the current to the relay is cut off. The armature is thus released and the contacts close again, so the relay comes on again and the contacts open, so the relay goes off . . .

This is very much like the astable circuit we described in Fig. 64. The relay does not settle in to one position but changes from *off* to *on* and back many times per second. This is basically how an electric buzzer works, and if you can imagine a hammer being fixed onto the armature and striking a bell as it is pulled up and released, then this is also how an electric bell works.

**Fig. 113**

# 10 Electronic Projects

Veroboard

**Fig. 114**

The circuits described in this chapter are adaptations of previous circuits, but re-designed to give slightly better performance. Since these circuits will be more useful in a compact form, we shall first describe a method for building circuits in a more compact way.

The circuits will be built on a special sort of printed circuit called *veroboard*. The picture is of a sheet of veroboard with a few components soldered onto it. The legs of each component are pushed through the holes in the top of the board . . .

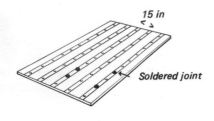

15 in

Soldered joint

**Fig. 115**

. . . and are soldered onto copper strips which are on the bottom of the board. The copper strips run in rows so that all the component legs on a particular row are joined together.

Obviously you have to work out very carefully where to put the components. Since this is quite difficult, we have provided a *layout* diagram as well as a circuit diagram for each project. These layout diagrams are views from the component side of the board. (When the board is turned over for soldering, this picure is inverted; the top becomes the bottom and the bottom becomes the top).

In the veroboard we use, the distance between the holes is 3·8 mm (0.15 in).

This is a side view of the components soldered onto the veroboard to show how they are mounted. They are only a few millimetres above the board, and may be standing upright or lying down. The components are pushed through from the top and soldered underneath, and *then* the excess wire is cut off, not before. The wire is removed with wire cutters, as close to the board as possible.

For transistors and diodes, which might be damaged by the heat of the soldering iron, use the methods described in Appendix III (page 58) *Soldering Techniques*. Mount these components about 1 cm above the board.

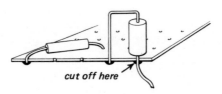

cut off here

**Fig. 116**

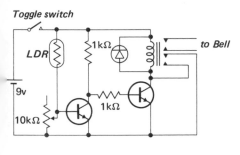

Fig. 117

### A Burglar Alarm

This circuit is basically that of Fig. 51. When the burglar walks in front of the *L.D.R.* the self-holding relay pulls up and the relay contacts can be used to operate a bell, buzzer or electronic siren (see Project 7) or a bulb to give visible warning instead.

The toggle switch is used to switch the battery off, when the circuit is not being used, and also to reset the circuit. The variable resistor is used to adjust the point at which the relay pulls up. The 10 kΩ resistor connected to the base of transistor $T_1$ as in Fig. 51 is not used now, to make the circuit more sensitive.

*Components List*
| | |
|---|---|
| 2 off 1 kΩ resistors | 1 off radiospares relay (Type 40) |
| 2 off *ZTX* 300 transistors | |
| 1 off OA 200 diode | 1 off *ORP* 12 *L.D.R.* |
| 1off 10 kΩ variable resistor | 1 off 9 V battery (*PP6*) |
| 1off *on/off* toggle switch | 1 off battery clip (*PP6*) |

This is the layout diagram, viewed from the component side. (We pretend that we can see through the board to the copper strips underneath)

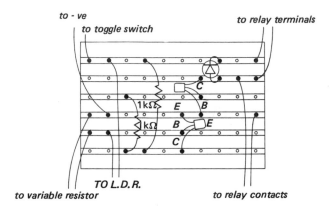

Fig. 118

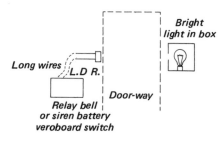

Fig. 119

This is a suggestion of how to set up the burglar alarm. The relay, bell or siren, battery, switch and veroboard are inside a box some distance from the *L.D.R.*

The light is placed inside a box so that the burglar cannot see it from the side, and the *L.D.R.* is mounted opposite a hole in the box on the other side of a passage or doorway.

43

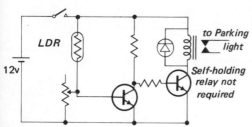

## Project 2: An Automatic Parking Light

The same circuit can be used to make a parking light for a motor car. Instead of going to a bell, the relay contacts go to a parking light, or to the car side-lights. When it is daylight, the relay is *off*, but at night the relay pulls up and switches on the car parking light or sidelights.

The circuit is shown as working off 12 volts, because we would expect it to run from the car battery itself.

The *L.D.R.* must be mounted so that daylight can fall upon it, but not light from the parking lamp itself, nor light from the headlamps of passing cars.

**Fig. 120**

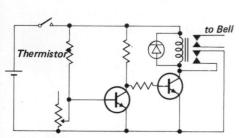

## Project 3: A Frost Warning Alarm

This circuit is the same as for the first project, except that the *L.D.R.* is replaced by the thermistor. The variable resistor is adjusted so that the relay pulls up when the temperature of the thermistor falls below freezing point. The thermistor is mounted outside, at ground level, while the relay, bell or siren, battery and so forth are inside the house. When the outside temperature falls below freezing point the alarm will sound.

**Fig. 121**

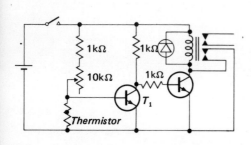

## Project 4: A Fire Alarm

This circuit is the same as for the third project, but with the thermistor and variable resistor swapped over. Notice the extra 1 kΩ resistor connected to the variable resistor. This is to stop the full battery voltage from reaching the base of transistor $T_1$, when the variable resistor is turned to zero resistance.

The relay will be *off* until the thermistor becomes hot, and then the relay will pull up and the bell will sound. The temperature at which the relay pulls up is adjusted with the variable resistor.

**Fig. 122**

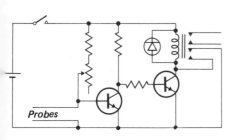

Probes

**Fig. 123**

**Project 5: A Rain Alarm**

This circuit is similar to Project 4, but with the thermistor replaced by two rain probes. These are two long copper rods mounted outside the house, which are parallel and as close as possible without touching.

Normally the relay is *off*, but if a single drop of rain falls onto the probes to join them together, the relay pulls up and sounds the alarm.

To make this circuit even more sensitive we have used a 100 kΩ variable resistor. The circuit still works with the 10 kΩ resistor, but is much less sensitive.

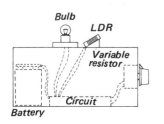

Bulb

LDR

Variable
resistor

Circuit

Battery

**Fig. 124**

**Project 6: An Electronic Candle**

The diagram shows a bulb in its holder mounted to face an *L.D.R.* In the box underneath is the circuit together with the battery, an *on/off* toggle switch and the variable resistor.

If the variable resistor is set correctly, the bulb will be *off*, but if a lighted match is brought up to the bulb, the light from the match falls on the *L.D.R.* and the bulb switches *on*. The bulb stays *on* even when the match is withdrawn, because the light from the bulb now falls on the *L.D.R.* The apparant effect is that the match has lit the bulb, just as a candle can be lit with a match!

To extinguish the candle, blow it out! Place your hand around the bulb as you blow, and thereby cut off the light getting to the *L.D.R.*

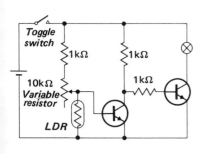

Toggle
switch

1kΩ        1kΩ

10kΩ                1kΩ
Variable
resistor

LDR

**Fig. 125**

This is the circuit of the electronic candle. It is basically the same as in Fig. 117, but the self-holding relay is replaced by the bulb once more.

The variable resistor is adjusted so that the bulb just stays *off*, but comes *on* when the lighted match is brought up to it, and then it stays *on*. You will need to experiment with the distance between the bulb and the *L.D.R.* to get the best effect.

This is the layout diagram:

*Components List*

| | | | |
|---|---|---|---|
| 3 off | 1kΩ resistors | 1 off | *ORP* 12 *L.D.R.* |
| 2 off | ZTX 300 transistors | 1 off | 6 volt 60 mA bulb |
| 1 off | 10 kΩ variable resistor | 1 off | bulb holder |
| 1 off | 9 volt battery (*PP6*) | 1 off | *on/off* toggle switch |
| 1 off | battery clip (*PP6*) | | |

Note that we have more than six different soldered connections to make in the circuit, so we have to use one of the copper strips *twice*. We thus separate the copper strip into two parts. This is done by rotating a 0·25 inch drill in the appropriate hole to cut the copper strip. (marked as *A* on the layout diagram)

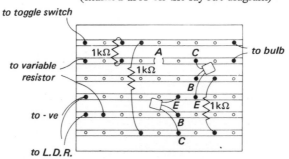

**Fig. 126**

---

### Project 7: An Electronic Siren

Instead of using a bell or buzzer as an audible warning, it is possible to make a siren. This is based on the astable circuit of Fig. 76. Then we used an earpiece to listen to the oscillations, but we must now use a loud-speaker to make a much louder sound. This works in the same way as the earpiece, but it has a very much smaller resistance, so we have to put it into the circuit in a different way.

We use the simple transistor invertor (transistor $T_3$) but with the loud-speaker connected instead of a resistor as shown. As the electric current is switched *on* and *off* in the speaker, a loud sound will be produced. Note the symbol for the loud-speaker.

We are not using a variable resistor, since we do not want to change the frequency of the note. The siren is switched on either through a toggle switch as shown, or by connecting the wires *P* and *Q* to the contacts of a relay, so that the siren comes on when the relay pulls up.

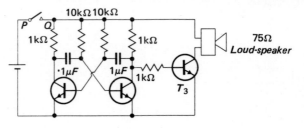

**Fig. 127**

This is the layout diagram of the siren.

*Components List*

| | | | |
|---|---|---|---|
| 3 off | 1 kΩ resistors | 2 off | 0·1 μF capacitors |
| 3 off | ZTX 300 transistors | 2 off | 10 kΩ resistors |
| 1 off | 75 to 85Ω loudspeaker | 1 off | toggle switch or relay contacts |
| 1 off | 9 volt battery (PP6) | | |
| 1 off | battery clip (PP6) | | |

Notice that the copper strips are cut at X and at Y

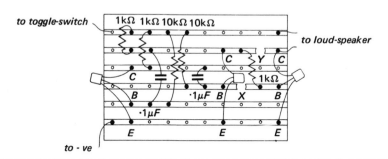

**Fig. 128**

### Project 8: An Electronic Organ

By adapting the siren circuit slightly we can make an electronic organ. Instead of a single resistor we use eight 'preset' variable resistors, which end at the terminals C, D, E, F, G, A, B, C. When the flying lead ending in a probe P is touched onto C, a note is sounded which can be adjusted to middle C of the piano. When P is touched onto terminal D, note D of the piano is sounded. Note the symbol for the preset resistor.

The electronic organ is tuned by adjusting the variable resistors in order, and it is played by touching the probe onto the terminals.

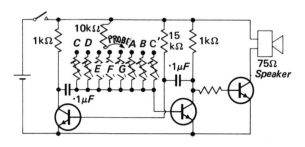

**Fig. 129**

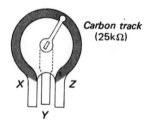

Carbon track (25kΩ)

**Fig. 130**

No layout diagram or list of components is provided, since the circuit is so similar to that of Project 7.
Similarly it is left to you to decide how to mount the variable resistors and how to make the key-board etc.

Since a set of eight variable resistor might be expensive, it is cheaper to use smaller ones, which are called 25kΩ skeleton presets. These have a carbon track as a resistor and adjustment is made with a small screw-driver.

## Project 9: A Metronome or Light Flasher

The flashing light of a police car or lighthouse has a long interval compared with the length of the flash, or as we say, it has a low *mark/space* ratio.

Here is a circuit for such a light flasher, and if a loud-speaker is used instead of a bulb, it can be used as a metronome for providing 'pips' at set intervals.

The time interval between flashes or 'pips' is set by the variable resistor, and can be altered from 0·5 seconds to 2 seconds.

No layout diagram is described since the circuit is so similar to that of Project 7.

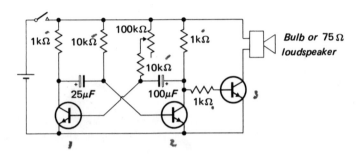

**Fig. 131**

## Project 10: A Time Switch

This circuit is basically that of Fig. 63.

When the circuit is switched on, the relay does not pull up immediately, but several seconds later, determined by the setting of the variable resistor.

Depending upon what is connected to the relay contacts, a light, bell, buzzer or siren then comes on. The relay is reset by switching off for about 1 minute or so, to allow the capacitor to discharge itself.

A scale marked off in seconds can be made and fixed so that the knob of the variable resistor indicates the time interval. This could then be used as a photographic timing device in a darkroom.

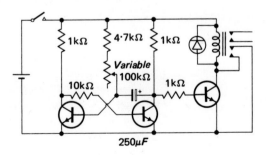

**Fig. 132**

### Project 11: A Sound Operated Switch

This circuit has a microphone (or an earpiece used as a microphone), followed by a two stage amplifier (similar to that of Fig. 90). This in turn is followed by a demodulator circuit, which turns the alternating voltages from the microphone into d.c. voltages. The louder the sound in the microphone, the greater will be this voltage. We can therefore use it to switch on a relay as shown. The relay can be connected to any device that we want to switch on, such as an electric motor to drive a small car.

The relay is a self-holding type, so that the circuit must be switched off to reset it.

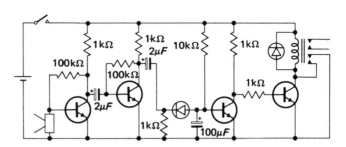

**Fig. 133**

### Project 12: An Intercom

The circuit is identical to that of Fig. 92. The difference introduced here, is to enable either end to be a speaker or a listener. This is done with a *two pole change-over* switch.

When the switch is up, the left-hand earpiece is the microphone and when the switch is down, the right-hand earpiece is the microphone. This is the 'remote' station, which can be some way from the main station. Since it is the person at the main station who switches over from speaking to listening, a special code is needed so that he knows when the remote station is ready to listen. This usually takes the form of saying 'Over,' whenever a speaker has finished.

A switch like this is called a *Double Pole, Double Throw* toggle switch.

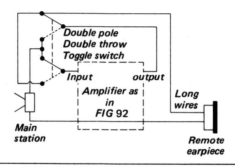

**Fig. 134**

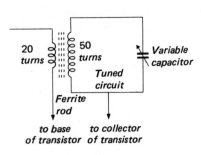

20 turns

50 turns

*Variable capacitor*

*Tuned circuit*

*Ferrite rod*

to base of transistor    to collector of transistor

**Fig. 135**

## Project 13: A Home Transmitter

This next project is a home radio transmitter. This will only work over a few metres since it is illegal to make a transmitter which could interfere with proper radio broadcasts. Nevertheless a commercial radio receiver will pick up the transmission.

The 'heart' of the transmitter is the tuned circuit. A simple winding on top of the first coil feeds back some of the alternating current from the collector into the base of the transistor. If the windings of the coils are right, we have positive feedback and the ferrite rod will produce a carrier wave.

By feeding an amplified speech audio frequency into the emitter of the transistor, the carrier wave is modulated like a real broadcasting station modulates its carrier wave.

To get the transmitter to work, switch on a commercial radio receiver to the medium waveband (about 300 metres), and tune it to where there is no commercial broadcast, then turn the volume control to maximum.

Get your transmitter close to the radio receiver and slowly tune the variable capacitor. When your transmitter emits a carrier wave equal to the frequency being received by the receiver, the latter will break out into a loud howl, because of acoustic feedback; if it does not do this, swap over the wires $A$ and $B$ of the 20 turn coil.

Now turn down the volume control and move back from the receiver until the howling stops. When you speak into your microphone, your voice will come from the receiver, loud but not clear. You are now 'on the air' with your own broadcasting station.

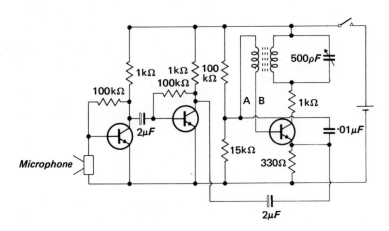

**Fig. 136**

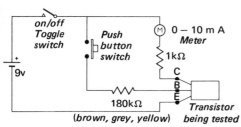

on/off
Toggle
switch

Push
button
switch

9v

180kΩ
(brown, grey, yellow)

Ⓜ 0 – 10 m A
Meter

1kΩ

C
B
E

Transistor
being tested

### Project 14: A Transistor and Diode Tester

Sometimes a transistor may have been put into a circuit the wrong way round, or it may have become over-heated whilst being soldered. It may be necessary to check that it is still working properly. To do this we use a circuit rather like that of Fig. 28, except that we use a meter to measure the current rather than a bulb.

The circuit is made up on tag-strip to show a different method of construction from Veroboard. The transistor to be tested is clipped into the circuit with three crocodile clips $C$, $B$ and $E$. Before the push-button is pressed, point $I$ is at a low voltage, so the transistor should be a high resistance and the current flowing into the collector should be very small. In practice a transistor should be rejected if it shows a current reading more than $0.1$ milliamp. Since the meter used has a full-scale deflection of 10 milliamps, this represents only a tiny movement of the meter needle. We call this current the *leakage current*.

The push button is then pressed to make point $I$ a high voltage. The meter reading should become somewhere between 2 and 9 milliamps. If it is less than 2 milliamps, the transistor should be rejected.

**Fig. 137**

This shows the layout diagram for tagstrip. If possible the circuit should be mounted in a box.

In order to test diodes, remember that they should have a low forward resistance and a high reverse resistance. Connect the diode between clips $C$ and $E$ only; the push button is not used for testing diodes. With the positive end of the diode connected to clip $E$, the diode should have a low resistance, so the meter reading should be *greater than* 8 milliamps. With the positive of the diode connected to $C$, the resistance should be large and the meter reading should be *less than* $0.1$ milliamp. Any diode outside these limits should not be used in circuits.

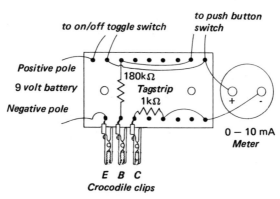

to on/off toggle switch

to push button switch

Positive pole
9 volt battery
Negative pole

180kΩ
Tagstrip
1kΩ

+ –

0 – 10 mA
Meter

E  B  C
Crocodile clips

**Fig. 138**

# 11 Computer Circuits

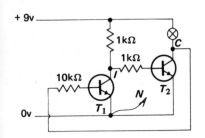

Fig. 139

This is the circuit diagram of the bistable switch of Fig. 53. Do you remember how it works?

It is stable in two positions, either with the bulb *off* or with the bulb *on*. The bistable switch is said to be *on* if the bulb is *on* and *off* if the bulb is *off*. At the moment we can switch the bistable *on* by touching the clip of lead $N$ to the point $I$.

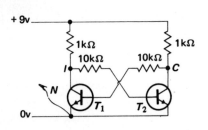

Fig. 140

This is the same circuit as above but with two changes. Instead of having the bulb as the load, we are using a 1 k$\Omega$ resistor, and so we must use a bigger base resistor, in this case 10 k$\Omega$. We have also drawn the circuit slightly differently with the first transistor turned round. We do this because it is easier to draw it like this.

We would still be able to switch the bistable *on* or *off* by tapping the clip of lead $N$ onto $I$ or $C$ as before, but we would not be able to see it change over now.

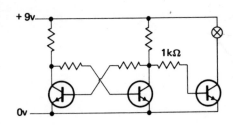

Fig. 141

So that we can tell whether the bistable is *on* or *off*, we use the simple circuit of Fig. 29. When $I$ is a high voltage, the bulb is *on*, and when $I$ is a low voltage, the bulb is *off*.

We are now back to the bistable switch of Fig. 139 but with the advantage that the loads of both transistors are the same, and it becomes easier to switch the bistable *on* and *off*.

In the next circuit we shall add two diodes, two small capacitors (0·01 $\mu F$) and two more resistors (10 k$\Omega$) in such a way that the bistable can be switched *on* or *off at the same input terminal*.

Make up this circuit on the soft-board, using the list of components as in Fig. 142. Keep all leads as long as possible. The bistable can be switched alternately *on* and *off* by tapping the clip of a flying lead $P$ onto the terminal $J$ as in the diagram.

When $P$ is touched onto $J$, $J$ becomes a high voltage so $K$ becomes a low voltage. As it goes from high to low, a *negative* pulse travels through both capacitors to the points $A$ and $B$. If the bistable is already *off*, then the point $B$ is at a high voltage (because it is connected to $I$) and this high positive voltage swamps the negative pulse that arrives through the capacitor. However, $A$ is at a low voltage (because it is connected to $C$), so the negative pulse is *not* swamped, but passed through the diode to the base of transistor $T_2$ and turns it *off*, so $C$ will become a high voltage and the bulb will come *on*.

Now $A$ is at a high voltage and $B$ at a low voltage, so the next time $P$ is tapped onto $J$, the negative pulse will travel through the *other* diode to the base of transistor $T_1$ and so the bistable will go *off* again.

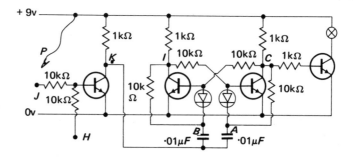

**Fig. 142**

Make up another bistable switch as in the diagram and connect its input terminal $L$ to the point $C$ of Fig. 142. Make sure that the positive lines are connected together, and the negative lines are connected together.

Now tap $P$ onto $J$ slowly, and watch what happens.

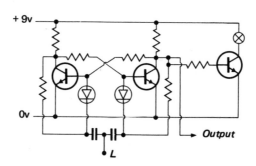

**Fig. 143**

53

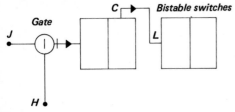

Gate

*C*

*Bistable switches*

*J*

*L*

*H*

**Fig. 144**

This is a simplified picture of what we have.

The first transistor is a *gate* (see Fig. 56). The output from this gate is connected to the input terminal of the first bistable. The output from this is fed to the input terminal of the second bistable.

Suppose that we start with both bistables in the *off* position. If a bulb is *on* we represent it with the digit '1', and if the bulb is *off* we represent it with the digit '0'.

To begin with we therefore have both bulbs *off* or '00'.

If *P* is tapped onto *J* just once, the first bistable comes *on* but the second does not alter . . . or '01'.

If *P* is tapped onto *J* once again, the first bistable goes *off* and in doing so puts the next bistable *on* . . . or '10'.

If *P* is tapped onto *J* once again, the first bistable comes *on* again, leaving the second bistable still *on* . . . or '11'.

If *P* is tapped onto *J* again, the first bistable goes *off*, and in doing so puts the second bistable *off* . . . or '00'.

If we had had another bistable connected to the output of the second bistable, it would have come *on* at the receipt of this fourth pulse.

The complete switching sequence would then be

0 0 0
0 0 1
0 1 0
0 1 1
1 0 0
1 0 1
1 1 0
1 1 1

Those who know how to count in *binary* will recognise this at once. We have made a *binary counter*.

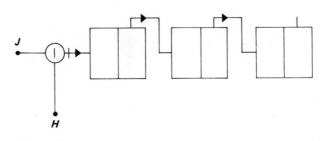

*J*

*H*

**Fig. 145**

54

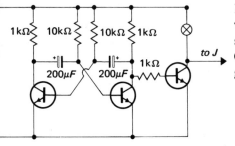

1kΩ   10kΩ   10kΩ   1kΩ

200μF   200μF   1kΩ

to J

**Fig. 146**

Rather than put the pulses in by hand, make up this astable circuit, which will provide a pulse every second or so. Notice that it is very similar to the astable circuits we have already studied (Fig. 64). Connect the output from the astable circuit to the input of the gate (*J*).

This is what we now have using our simplified symbols. We call these *logic diagrams*.

As the astable switches *off* and *on* it provides pulses to the gate. Provided *H* is at a low voltage these pulses get through to the set of bistables so that they will slowly count in binary. To stop the pulses connect *H* to the positive line. Then the gate will close (as described in Fig. 56) so the pulses will not get through.

By using the *L.D.R.* between *H* and the positive line, and a variable resistor between *H* and the negative line, we have a way of using light to open or close the gate.

If the setting of the variable resistor is correct, the gate will be open if it is dark, but will close if it is bright. So the counter will only be counting if it is dark.

There are many many more ways of putting these switching circuits together to make binary counters, adders and timers, or to make machines which will solve logical problems, or even to make a computer to add, subtract, multiply and divide. If you would like to go on to these exciting possibilities you must know some special mathematics called *Boolean Algebra*, which is taught in many schools in *Modern Mathematics* courses. Those who wish to go on and build some of these circuits, should obtain the book *Computer Models* by A. Wilkinson.

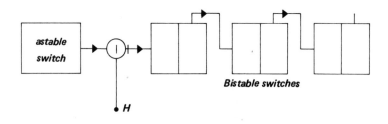

astable switch

*H*

*Bistable switches*

**Fig. 147**

# Appendix I
## Resistor Colour Code

The value of each resistor in *ohms* is indicated by three coloured bands around it. There may be a fourth band of silver or gold which indicates how accurately the resistor has been made, ignore this band.

The first two bands represent numbers according to the following code. The third coloured band represents a multiplier.

| | | | | |
|---|---|---|---|---|
| *Black* | represents | 0 | (multiplier | x 1) |
| *Brown* | represents | 1 | (multiplier | x 10) |
| *Red* | represents | 2 | (multiplier | x 100) |
| *Orange* | represents | 3 | (multiplier | x 1 000) |
| *Yellow* | represents | 4 | (multiplier | x 10 000) |
| *Green* | represents | 5 | (multiplier | x 100 000) |
| *Blue* | represents | 6 | (multiplier x | 1 000 000) |
| *Purple* or | represents | 7 | (multiplier x | 10 000 000) |
| *Violet* | | | | |
| *Grey* | represents | 8 | | |
| *White* | represents | 9 | | |

| | | | |
|---|---|---|---|
| Thus 10 000 ohm is | *Brown* | (first digit is | 1) |
| | *Black* | (second digit is | 0) |
| | *Orange* | (multiplier is x 1 000) | |
| 4·7 kΩ is 4 700 Ω is | *Yellow* | | 4) |
| | *Purple* | | 7) |
| | *Red* | ( x 100) | |

| | | |
|---|---|---|
| Other resistors we have used are | 10Ω | (brown, black, black) |
| | 100Ω | (brown, black, brown) |
| | 1 kΩ | (brown, black, red) |
| | 10 kΩ | (brown, black, orange) |
| | 100 kΩ | (brown, black, yellow) |
| | 47 Ω | (yellow, purple, black) |
| | 4·7 kΩ | (yellow, purple, red) |
| | 180 kΩ | (brown, grey, yellow) |
| | 15 kΩ | (brown, green, orange) |

# Appendix II
## Circuit Symbols

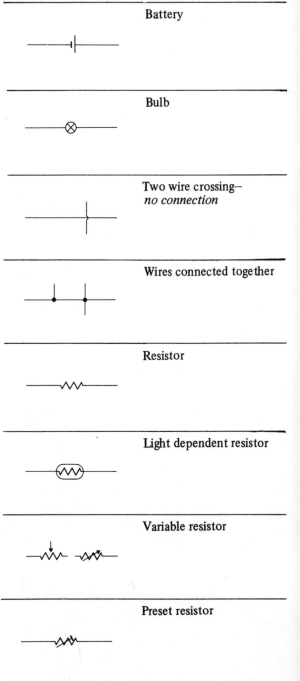

Battery

Bulb

Two wire crossing—
*no connection*

Wires connected together

Resistor

Light dependent resistor

Variable resistor

Preset resistor

# Circuit Symbols

Thermistor

Logic symbol for *gate*

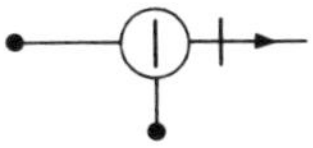

Diode

Logic symbol for
*bistable switch*

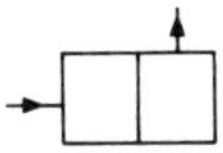

Small capacitor (usually
less than 1 $\mu$ F)

Microphone

Electrolytic capacitor

Earpiece

Transistor

Loudspeaker

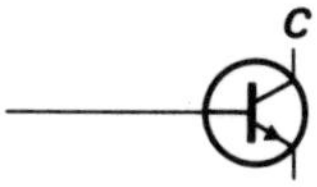

Coil wound on ferrite rod

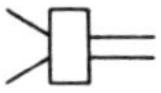

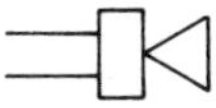

*on/off* Toggle switch

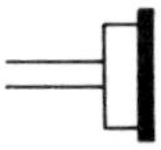

Variable capacitor

Relay and Contacts

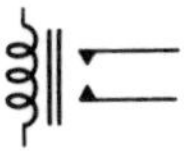

# Appendix III
## Soldering Techniques

### 1 General Points

Is the soldering iron *hot*? (Does a piece of solder melt instantly when touched onto the iron?)

Is the soldering iron *clean*? (i.e. not covered with a black crust, but looking bright and shiny?)

Are the pin and the wires *clean*? If not rub them with emery paper.

### 2 Components and wires not likely to be damaged by heat

Wrap the end of the component lead half-way round the pin, as in the diagram. Do not wrap it round the pin more than this.

Touch the soldering iron onto the joint.

Push a small amount of resin-cored solder onto the joint to touch the iron and the joint.

Wait till the solder melts and flows over the joint.

Remove the solder and the soldering iron and blow onto the joint to cool it. Do not touch it until it has gone hard.

When it has cooled, wiggle the wire to see if it is firm. Inspect the soldered joint to see if it is bright and shiny. If the wire is loose and the joint looks dull and crinkly, suspect a *dry joint* and resolder it.

*Do not* carry solder to the joint with the soldering iron. The resin flux will evaporate and a possible dry joint will be made.

*Do not* make 'mid-air' connections. Always solder onto a pin.

### 3 Components likely to be damaged by heat (e.g. transistors and diodes)

*Do not* wrap lead around the pin, instead get a blob of solder firmly soldered onto the pin to begin with.

Hold the leg of the transistor or diode being soldered with pliers.

Touch the lead onto the previously soldered pin.

Touch the soldering iron onto the joint until the solder flows over the lead.

Remove the soldering iron and blow hard on the joint to cool it.

Test to see if the joint is firm.

Another simple way of preventing over-heating is to place a small piece of potato onto the lead being soldered as in the diagram. This is a good way of soldering transistors onto veroboard.

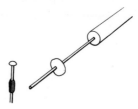

# Appendix IV
## What Went Wrong?

If you get a circuit that does not work as it should, *find out why* before you go on to the next circuit. Follow the pattern described here.

**1 Visual Check**

(a) Have you connected the battery? Is it the right way round?

(b) Is the circuit exactly as your circuit diagram? Are there any wires or components missed out. Are there wires or components, which should have been taken out, which are still there?

(c) Is there a break in the wiring or has a lead broken off anywhere?

(d) Are all soldered joints firm and bright and shiny. If not, resolder the joint, as it may be a dry joint.

(e) Have you read the colour code of the resistors correctly? Check that each resistor is correct.

(f) Have you put the transistor in the right way round? Check each leg of the transistor. Refer back to Fig. 24, to check on which leg is which.

(g) Have you put the electrolytic capacitors in the right way round?

(h) Is the battery flat? Will it light up a bulb placed across it?

**2 Component Check**

(a) Resistors and capacitors
These are most unlikely to go wrong. If you have tried everything else, then replace each resistor and capacitor with another of the same value.

(b) Diodes and Transistors
These may be damaged by heat (from the soldering iron) and by having the full battery voltage applied directly to them or by being connected into a circuit the wrong way round. Remove the suspect transistor or diode from the circuit and test it with a transistor checker (see Project 14, page 51). Alternatively make up a simple circuit with a bulb (e.g. Fig. 28) to check.

**3 Problems peculiar to amplifiers**

Circuits containing amplifiers have their own problems in that a transistor may be *wrongly biased*. Measure the voltage across the transistor with a voltmeter (0—10 volts), between the collector (positive of the voltmeter) and the emitter (negative of the voltmeter). It should be between 3 and 6 volts.

If this voltage is *greater than 6 volts, reduce* the 100 kΩ biasing resistor (see Fig. 88) to 82 kΩ or less.

If this voltage is *less than 3 volts* (and the battery is not flat) *increase* the bias resistor to 120kΩ or more.

Now check that the emitter-collector voltage is between 3 and 6 volts, as it should be.

# Appendix V
## Notes for the Teacher

R.S. Components Ltd
P.O. Box 427
13-17, Epworth Street
London E.C. 2

This book is designed so that it can be used by pupils working alone or in pairs without help from the teacher. Where a school has a time-table period set aside for project work or hobbies period or 'activity session', this book, a kit of components and a set of tools can be given to each group, who can then work through it unsupervised. In some schools, where this type of activity is left as an 'out-of-school' pursuit, the same principle may be employed.

Some schools, wishing to introduce electronics to the whole class, could devote the science or craft practical periods of a whole term to working through this book, the teacher's help only being needed occasionally. This is the most obvious way for schools following Theme 5·4 of the Nuffield Secondary Science Course.

Whatever happens it must be appreciated that this book is intended to lead into electronics project work. After attempting some of the projects described in the later chapters, pupils should be encouraged to try others taken from other books or periodicals. As a start the following may be recommended.

For computer circuits: *Computer Models*
by A. Wilkinson
For general ideas: *Practical Electronics*
*Practical Wireless*
*Radio Constructor*

The first eight chapters of this book constitute a basic introduction to electronics. It is possible to learn something by reading through these chapters only, but for the greatest benefit, it is necessary for the reader to have a basic kit of parts, and for him to work through the book step-by-step. This basic kit may be obtained from

*NESLO* Electronics
5, Field House Close
Hepscott Northumberland.

If it is planned to have three or more basic kits, it becomes more economical for teachers to obtain their own components and make up their own kits. Most of the components used in the basic kit are also used in the projects described in the later chapters. They are nearly all obtained from

### Basic Kit Parts (Chapter 1 to 8)

| Number required per kit | Component |
|---|---|
| 1 | 10 $\Omega$ Resistor (½W) |
| 1 | 47 $\Omega$ Resistor (½W) |
| 1 | 100 $\Omega$ Resistor (½W) |
| 3 | 1 k$\Omega$ Resistor (½W) |
| 1 | 4·7 k$\Omega$ Resistor (½W) |
| 2 | 10 k$\Omega$ Resistor (½W) |
| 3 | 100 k$\Omega$ Resistor (½W) |
| 1 | Thermistor |
| 1 | Variable Resistor |
| 1 | 220 pF capacitor |
| 2 | 0·01 $\mu$ F capacitor |
| 2 | 0·1 $\mu$ F capacitor |
| 3 | 2 $\mu$ F capacitor |
| 2 | 100 $\mu$ F capacitor |
| 1 | Variable capacitor (500pF) |
| 1 | Diode |
| 1 | Bulb |
| 1 | Bulb-holder |
| 1 | Knob |
| 1 | Ferrite rod |
| 1 | Battery (PP6) |
| 1 | Battery clip |
| | Solder |
| | Flexible wires (for flying leads) |
| | Connecting wire (between brass pins) |
| 4 | Crocodile clips |
| 3 | Transistors (ZTX 300) (BC 108) |
| 2 | Woodscrews (½" Rdhead, No 6) |
| | Brass panel pins (¾", 20 SWG) |
| 1 | Softboard (25 cm x 20 cm) |
| 2 (or 1) | Crystal Earpieces |
| 1 | Light dependent resistors (ORP 12, or equivalent) |

Any school may open an account with this firm and obtain copies of their catalogue upon application. The components are ordered under a special 'code-name' given after each component.

| upplier (and RS code name) | Number per pk |
|---|---|
| .S. Pk (½W) Res (10 Ω) | 5 |
| .S. Pk (½W) Res (47 Ω) | 5 |
| .S. Pk (½W) Res (100 Ω) | 5 |
| .S. Pk (½W) Res (1 kΩ) | 5 |
| .S. Pk (½W) Res (4·7 kΩ) | 5 |
| .S. Pk (½W) Res (10 kΩ) | 5 |
| .S. Pk (½W) Res (100 kΩ) | 5 |
| .S. Pk thermistors (TH3) | 3 |
| .S. Midget Lin (10 kΩ) | 1 |
| .S. Pk P.S. caps (220pF) | 5 |
| .S. Pk L.V. discs (18V 0·01 $\mu$ F) | 5 |
| .S. Pk L.V. discs (30V 0·1 $\mu$ F) | 5 |
| .S. Pk Tubes (2 $\mu$ F, 150V) | 3 |
| .S. Pk Tubes (100 $\mu$ F, 25V) | 3 |
| Ienry's Radio | |
| .S. 1GP7 diode | 1 |
| .S. Box M.E.S. Bulb (6V 0·06A) | 10 |
| .S. M.E.S. Battenholder (Black) | 1 |
| .S. GS 11 knob | 1 |
| .S. Ferrite (6 x $\frac{3}{8}$") | 1 |
| Ibtain locally | |
| .S. Twin Miniature Press Stud | 1 |
| .S. Reel Solder (18 SWG) | ½lb |
| .S. Reel Single PVC stranded (specify colour) | 25m |
| .S. T/C wire (22 SWG) | ½lb |
| .S. Standard Croc. Clips | 12 |
| IEL Components LTD. | |
| .S. Components Ltd. | |
| Ibtain locally | |
| Ibtain locally | |
| Ibtain locally | |
| Ienry's Radio | |
| Ienry's Radio. | |

## Special Components (Chapter 9 to 11, excluding resistors etc.)

| Components | Supplier |
|---|---|
| Relay (12V, 185Ω) | RS. Relay Type 40 |
| on/off Toggle switch | RS. Toggles (SPST) |
| Intercom c/o switch | RS. Toggles (DPDT) |
| Transistor Tester push-button switch | RS. Min Push Make |
| Preset variable resistors (for electronic organ) | RS. Skeleton Presets (25 kΩ) |
| 100 kΩ variable resistors | RS. Midget Lin (100 kΩ) |
| 0-10 mA meter | Henry's Radio |
| Veroboard (0.15" matrix) | R.S. Stripboard |
| Loudspeaker (75Ω) | Henry's Radio |

Henry's Radio also supply individual resistors, capacitors and so on. Their complete catalogue is obtainable (not free) from

Henry's Radio Ltd
303, Edgware Road
London W2

WEL Components Ltd. are suppliers of the Ferranti ZTX 300 transistor and prices may be obtained from them by request. Their address is

WEL Components Ltd.
5, Loverock Road
Reading

A suitable alternative transistor is the BC 108 now available from R.S. Components Ltd.

The transistor does *not* have to be this particular one. All of the circuits have been designed to work with *any* silicon planar *NPN* transistor having a current gain between 50 and 150. Similarly *any* point contact germanium diode will do in place of the diode used in Chapter 8 (in the radio receiver), whilst *any* silicon junction diode which can carry 60 mA will do for Chapter 2 and in the binary counter in Chapter 11. Teachers may wish to buy such transistors and diodes as 'Un-marked, Un-tested' devices from suppliers such as
Bi-Pack Semiconductors
P.O. Box 6
Ware
Hertfordshire

The individual devices will then have to be tested (see Project 14) before being issued to pupils.

The most expensive single item in the basic kit is the light dependent resistor. Since it is possible to break the legs off this device by careless handling, teachers may wish to mount it in a more robust way, possibly on veroboard, with two pieces of wire as 'false legs'.

To cut the cost a little, teachers may wish to note that pupils only require *two* earpieces for a small part of the course. It is possible to supply *one* such earpiece to each pupil and keep one spare, to be borrowed when required.

We have already explained our preference for using a soldering method of construction, but some teachers may not like this, opting instead for a 'no-soldering' method.

One of the simplest of these is 'S-dec', where the components are pushed into holes on a special deck, where they are held in place by phosphor-bronze strips, which also make electrical connection with the other components. Enquiries should be made to

S.D.C. Electronics (Sales) Ltd
34, Arkwright
Astmoor Industrial Estate
Runcorn
Cheshire

Some teachers may wish to make their own versions of this by fixing brass eyelets in peg-board, and holding them in place with plastic golf tees. This method is described in a leaflet obtainable from

Mullard Educational Services
Mullard Ltd
Mullard House
Torrington Place
London WC1

This firm also provides circuits for many interesting projects, which may be obtained for a very small charge on application.

Other 'no-soldering' methods are: holding the components in flexible springs mounted on peg-board (Griffin and George Ltd.) or with spring clips mounted on peg-board (Philips Electronic Engineer). Alternatively the components may be mounted on special holders and just clipped into place on a previously prepared board (Radionic).

The advantages of such methods are the extra safety and lower cost, since components are more easily re-used. However, the saving in money has to be off-set against the teacher's time in preparing the boards. Even the soldering method we have used, enables the same components to be re-used many times, if they are carefully un-soldered from the board after use, and, apart from teaching pupils the art of soldering, once this technique has been mastered, the danger of poor connections is virtually eliminated, whereas it is a constant threat in most no-soldering methods.

Whatever method is finally adopted, it is essential that pupils can initially build up their circuits exactly as the circuit diagram. Children just beginning electronics will have enough problems, without adding the difficulty of translating a two dimensional diagram into a three dimensional circuit.

For the soldering method we have used, the following tools are required.
20 or 25 watt electric soldering iron
Electricians 'tapered nose' pliers
Wire cutters (often referred to as 'side cutters')
Wire strippers (optional)
Small screw-driver.